DEPARTMENT OF NATURAL RESOURCES
WARREN T. HANNUM, *Director*

STATE OF CALIFORNIA
EARL WARREN, *Governor*

DIVISION OF MINES
Ferry Building, San Francisco 11
OLAF P. JENKINS, *Chief*

San Francisco]

BULLETIN 141

[September, 1948

GEOLOGIC GUIDEBOOK

ALONG HIGHWAY 49—SIERRAN GOLD BELT

THE MOTHER LODE COUNTRY

(CENTENNIAL EDITION)

Prepared under the direction of

OLAF P. JENKINS

Price $1.50

Contributing Authors

CHARLES V. AVERILL
OLIVER E. BOWEN, JR.
JOHN A. BURGESS

RICHARD A. CRIPPEN, JR.
DONALD C. CUTTER
FRANKLIN FENENGA
ROBERT F. HEIZER

DOROTHY G. JENKINS
OLAF P. JENKINS
CLARENCE A. LOGAN

A, LOOKING NORTHEAST TOWARD HARRY L. ENGLEBRIGHT DAM

Structure was dedicated to the memory of Harry L. Englebright, member of Congress, 1926-43, by the California Hydraulic Miners Association and approved by act of Congress in November 1945. This dam is one of several constructed for the dual purpose of catching debris from upstream hydraulic operations and impounding water for irrigation. *Photo by courtesy of George W. Hallock, State Mining Board.*

B, LOOKING NORTHEAST TOWARD MALAKOFF HYDRAULIC PIT AT NORTH BLOOMFIELD, NEVADA COUNTY.
Photo by courtesy of George W. Hallock

A, PANORAMIC VIEW TOWARD THE EAST

From rhyolite remnant on resurrected Eocene surface one mile east of Angels Camp. Other remnants of rhyolite tuff may be seen in the middle distance. *Photo by Olaf P. Jenkins.*

B, THE "MOTHER LODE"

Prominent quartz outcrops of the Mother Lode system as seen at the Harvard mine near Jamestown. *Photo by Olaf P. Jenkins.*

C, "TOMBSTONE ROCK" OF VOLCANIC AGGLOMERATE

Occurs one mile west of Copperopolis on the Farmington road. *Photo by Olaf P. Jenkins.*

D, SMALL ANTICLINE IN SLATE ALONG MARIPOSA CREEK

Folds are along actual slate beds and not along slaty cleavage lines. *Photo by Olaf P. Jenkins.*

E, TYPICAL VIEW OF THE SIERRAN FOOTHILLS

Near Mount Gaines mine, Hornitos district, Mariposa County. *Photo by courtesy of Francis Frederick.*

F, UNDERGROUND VIEW

In Alhambra mine near Garden Valley, El Dorado County. Note the free gold showing in patches in white quartz. *Photo by courtesy of Francis Frederick.*

LETTER OF TRANSMITTAL

To His Excellency
The Honorable Earl Warren
Governor of the State of California

DEAR SIR:

I have the honor to transmit herewith Bulletin 141, "Geologic Guidebook Along Highway 49—Sierran Gold Belt", prepared under the direction of Olaf P. Jenkins, Chief of the Division of Mines. The volume contains a series of geologic maps covering the entire highway, a strip of country 277 miles in length. Numerous photographs and other illustrations accompany the articles which make up this bulletin. The book represents the CENTENNIAL EDITION of the Division of Mines, describing THE MOTHER LODE COUNTRY. It has been carefully compiled from various published and unpublished sources of information supplemented by notes taken during field investigations carried on particularly for this volume. Besides the ten different authors who have written the chapters of this bulletin, a score of other mining men and geologists have contributed information.

Bulletin 141 is a semi-technical treatise prepared to serve as a guide to the traveler who is desirous of information concerning the mines, minerals, and rocks of the region, as well as the old structures erected during the Gold Rush Days. It is not merely intended for use during the Centennial celebrations, but should serve as a basis for future studies and investigations for many years to come.

Respectfully submitted,

WARREN T. HANNUM
Director, Department of
Natural Resources

August 1, 1948

First Printing—September 1948
Second Printing—February 1949
Third Printing—March 1953
Fourth Printing—July 1955

CONTENTS

———

CALIFORNIA IN RELIEF

SHOWING HIGHWAY 49 THROUGH
THE MOTHER LODE

FROM PHOTOGRAPH OF
MODEL MADE BY N. F. DRAKE
1896

0   50   100   150   200

SCALE IN MILES

Highway 49 shown as white line

PREFACE

The Centennial Celebration of the discovery of gold at Coloma by James W. Marshall on January 24, 1848, has stimulated renewed interest in the Mother Lode of California and has brought forth a number of new books, pamphlets and stories of the early pioneer days. Most of this literature has to do with the history, life, and romance of the Gold Rush period which vividly stamped upon the new western state a personality which has by no means been erased during the past century of industrial development. Few persons who enter the Sierran Gold Belt, however, appreciate the full significance of its mineral wealth, gain a clear picture of its extent and importance, or understand why this district is credited with having built the very foundation of the State's civilization even as it still contributes to the firmness of its industry and character.

The position of the mines and quarries, the importance of the mineral deposits, and the geologic reasons for their being are all features which this Guidebook has endeavored to present. The traveler who is desirous of information rather than speed can get a better understanding of the region if he follows a map prepared with an accompanying description logged carefully as to mileage.

The charm of the old mining towns, which harmonize so perfectly with the natural loveliness of the Sierran foothills, is due largely to the surviving stone and brick structures of pioneer days. These old buildings, many of which are now in ruins, stand as mute evidence of the early development of what is now called industrial minerals. Treatment of this subject shows how the value of natural resources of the country were immediately realized by the earliest settlers.

In order to orient the reader as to the nature of the Sierra Nevada and the place it occupies in relation to history, civilization, and economics, several special articles have been contributed by various authors.

To facilitate the reading of this Guidebook, especially while traveling, footnote references and acknowledgments have been largely deleted from the text. The published Geologic Folios, Professional Papers, and other published reports of the United States Geological Survey, together with unpublished maps and reports prepared by that agency in cooperation with the State Division of Mines, have formed the background of the areal geology for the region. This has been very materially supplemented by the unpublished work and advice of Dr. N. L. Taliaferro of the University of California, who has spent many years mapping the geology of the region west of the Mother Lode. For the area between Jacksonville and Angels Camp, unpublished geologic maps were supplied by Federal geologists George Heyl, John Eric, Arvid Stromquist, C. M. Swinney, and J. H. Wiese. The mapping between Jackson and Plymouth was supplemented by the field data of T. C. Slater, who also supplied data on the Central Eureka mine. Information concerning the mines was generously provided by the following: W. A. Simpkins of the Empire Star Mines Company, Ltd.; C. C. Cushwa of the Spring Hill mine; Neil O'Donnell of the Idaho Maryland Mines Corporation; C. A. Bennett and H. U. Maxfield of the Sixteen to One mine; D. C. Peacock of the Eagle-Shawmut mine; Mark Eudey of the Kennedy mine; J. A. Burgess of the Carson Hill mine; P. R. Bradley, Jr. of the Harvard mine; L. A. Parsons of the Calaveras Cement Company; T. S. O'Brien of the Keystone mine; C. E. Crandall of the Original Amador mine; O. E. Schiffner of the Lava Cap mine; and Francis Frederick, Consulting Geologist and Mining Engineer.

It was necessary, in the compilation of the strip maps, to adjust all the geology to fit the newly acquired base maps, i.e. the United States Forest Service planimetric quadrangles and the new topographic sheets (for the most part in the early stages of preparation) of the Federal Geological Survey. An effort was made to include the names and locations of the older abandoned settlements as well as the existing towns. The principal mines and mineral deposits are shown. The locations of the historic monuments are indicated and mileage is shown for use in location while traveling. In addition, symbols have been employed to show the type of early structure described in the text on this subject.

OLAF P. JENKINS
Chief, Division of Mines

Ferry Building, San Francisco
May 10, 1948

PUBLICATIONS CONSULTED

General Historical Interest

BAILEY, PAUL D., Sam Brannan and the Mormons: Westernlore Press, 187 pp., Los Angeles, 1943.

BANCROFT, HUBERT H., History of California: A. L. Bancroft and Co. and The History Co., 7 vols., San Francisco, 1884-1890.

CLELAND, ROBERT G., A history of California, the American period: The MacMillan Co., 512 pp., New York, 1922.

DRURY, AUBREY, California, an intimate guide: Harper and Bros., 592 pp., New York, 1947.

GLASSCOCK, C. B., A golden highway: The Bobbs-Merrill Co., 313 pp., Indianapolis, 1934.

HUNT, ROCKWELL D., California the golden: Silver, Burdette and Co., 362 pp., New York and Boston, 1911.

RENSCH, H. E., HOOVER, MILDRED BROOKE, and others, Historic spots in California, valley and Sierran counties: Stanford Univ. Press and Cambridge Univ. Press, 568 pp., Palo Alto and Cambridge, 1933.

ROBERTS, BRIGHAM H., The Mormon battalion: Deseret News, 96 pp., Salt Lake City, 1919.

WESTON, OTHETO, Mother Lode album: Stanford Univ. Press, 177 pp., 2 pls., 204 photos, Palo Alto, 1948.

The Gold Rush Period

BEKEART, PHILLIP B., James W. Marshall, discoverer of gold: Soc. California Pioneers Quarterly, vol. 1, no. 3, pp. 3-43, San Francisco, September 1924.

BORTHWICK, J. D., Three years in California: W. Blackwood and Sons, 384 pp., Edinburgh and London, 1857. Reprinted 1917 as *The Gold Hunters* edited by Horace Kephart: Outing Pub. Co., Cleveland and New York.

BUCKBEE, EDNA B., The saga of old Tuolumne: R. R. Wilson, 526 pp., New York, 1935.

BUFFUM, E. GOULD, Six months in the gold mines: Richard Bentley, 244 pp., London, 1850.

CALIFORNIA HISTORICAL SOCIETY, Centennial papers: Spec. Pub. 21, 56 pp., San Francisco, 1947.

CENDRARS, BLAISE, Sutters gold: Harper and Bro's., 179 pp., New York and London, 1926. Translated from the French by Henry L. Stuart.

COY, OWEN C., Gold days: Powell Pub. Co., 381 pp., Los Angeles, 1929 (1934).

DANA, JULIAN, Sutter of California: Halcyon Press (Blue Ribbon Books, Inc.), 413 pp., New York, 1934.

HULBERT, ARCHER B., Forty-niners: Little, Brown and Co., 362 pp., New York and Boston, 1911.

JACKSON, J. H.: Anybody's gold: D. Appleton-Century Co., 445 pp., New York, 1941.

JACKSON, J. H., Tintypes in gold: The MacMillan Co., 191 pp., New York, 1939.

JOHNSTONE, PHILIP, Lost and living cities of the California gold rush, California centennials guide: Touring Bureau, Automobile Club of Southern California, 61 pp., Los Angeles, 1948.

PAUL, RODMAN W., California gold: Harvard Univ. Press, 380 pp., Cambridge, Mass., 1947.

QUIETT, GLENN C., Pay dirt, a panorama of American gold rushes: D. Appleton-Century Co., Inc., 506 pp., New York and London, 1936.

STELLMAN, LOUIS J., Mother Lode, the story of California's gold rush days: Harr-Wagner Pub. Co., 304 pp., San Francisco, 1934.

WHITE, STEWART EDWARD, The forty-niners: Yale Univ. Press, 273 pp., New Haven, 1918.

Mines and Minerals

ANONYMOUS, California's debt to the miner: Pacific Gas and Electric Progress, vol. 1, no. 8, p. 2, 1924.

AVERILL, CHARLES V., and others, Placer mining for gold in California: California Div. Mines Bull. 135, 377 pp., 1946.

AVERILL, CHARLES V., Strategic minerals of the Sacramento district, California: California Div. Mines Rept. 39 pp. 71-76, 1943.

BROWNE, J. ROSS, Mineral resources of the states and territories west of the Rocky Mountains for 1867: U. S. Treasury Dept., 367 pp., Washington, D. C., 1868.

CALIFORNIA MINERS ASSOCIATION, California mines and minerals: California Miners Association, 445 pp., San Francisco, 1899.

DAVIS, WILLIAM MORRIS, The lakes of California: California Div. Mines Rept. 29, pp. 75-238, 1933. . . . California Jour. Mines and Geology, vol. 44, pp. 201-242, 1948.

DE GROOT, HENRY, El Dorado County: California Min. Bur. Rept. 10, pp. 169-182, 1890.

HANKS, HENRY G., Gold nuggets: California Min. Bur. Rept. 2, pp. 147-150, 1882.

HAUSMANN, A., and others, Copper resources of California: California Min. Bur. Bull. 50, 275 pp., 1908.

JULIHN, C. E., and HORTON, F. W., Mines of the southern Mother Lode region, pt. 1: U. S. Bur. Mines Bull. 413, 136 pp., 1938.

JULIHN, C. E., and HORTON, F. W., Mines of the southern Mother Lode region, pt. 2: U. S. Bur. Mines Bull. 424, 173 pp., 1940.

LOGAN, CLARENCE A., The Mother Lode gold belt of California: California Div. Mines Bull. 108, 240 pp., 1934.

LOGAN, CLARENCE A., Tuolumne County: California Div. Mines Rept. 24, pp. 3-53, 1928.

RICKARD, THOMAS A., A History of American mining: McGraw-Hill Book Co., Inc., 419 pp., New York and London, 1932.

RICKARD, THOMAS A., The reopening of old mines along the Mother Lode: Min. and Sci. Press, vol. 112, pp. 935-939, 1916.

TUCKER, W. BURLING, Amador County: California Min. Bur. Rept. 14, pp. 3-54, 1914.

Geology and Mining Engineering

DURRELL, CORDELL, Geology of the quartz crystal mines near Mokelumne Hill, Calaveras County, California: California Div. Mines Rept. 40 pp. 423-433, 1944.

FAIRBANKS, HAROLD W., Geology of the Mother Lode region: California Min. Bur. Rept. 10, pp. 23-90, 1 map, 31 figs., 1890.

HULIN, CARLTON D., A Mother Lode gold ore: Econ. Geology, vol. 23, no. 4, pp. 348-355, June 1930.

JOHNSTON, GEORGE, Brief history of concentration and description of the Johnston concentrator: In California mines and minerals, pp. 439-441, California Miners Association, San Francisco, 1899.

KNOPF, ADOLPH, The Mother Lode system of California: U. S. Geol. Survey Prof. Paper 157, 85 pp., 1929.

LAWSON, A. C., The Sierra Nevada: California Univ. Chronicle, vol. 23, pp. 130-149, 1921.

LINDGREN, WALDEMAR, U. S. Geol. Survey, Colfax folio (no. 66), 12 pp., 4 maps, 1897.

LINDGREN, WALDEMAR, U. S. Geol. Survey Atlas, Sacramento folio (no. 5), 5 pp., 4 maps, 1894.

LINDGREN, WALDEMAR, The Tertiary gravels of the Sierra Nevada, California: U. S. Geol. Survey Prof. Paper 73, 222 pp., 1911.

LINDGREN, WALDEMAR, and TURNER, H. W., Placerville folio (no. 3), 5 pp., 4 maps, 1894.

RANSOME, F. L., U. S. Geol. Survey Atlas, Mother Lode district folio (no. 63), 11 pp., 8 maps, 1897.

TALIAFERRO, NICHOLAS L., Manganese deposits of the Sierra Nevada; their genesis and metamorphism: California Div. Mines Bull. 125, pp. 277-332, 1943.

TURNER, H. W., U. S. Geol. Survey Atlas, Bidwell Bar folio (no. 43), 8 pp., 3 maps, 1 pl., 1898. . . . Downieville folio (no. 37), 10 pp., 4 maps, 1 pl., 1897. . . . Jackson folio (no. 11), 8 pp., 4 maps, 1894.

TURNER, H. W., and LINDGREN, WALDEMAR, U. S. Geol. Survey Atlas, Smartsville folio (no. 18), 8 pp., 4 maps, 1895.

TURNER, H. W., and RANSOME, F. L., U. S. Geol. Survey Atlas, Big Trees folio (no. 51), 10 pp., 3 maps, 1 pl., 1898.

TURNER, F. W., and RANSOME, F. L., U. S. Geol. Survey Atlas, Sonora folio (no. 41), 9 pp., 4 maps, 1897.

SIERRAN ROADS OF TODAY AND YESTERDAY

By Dorothy G. Jenkins

Highway 49, popularly known as the Mother Lode Highway, begins at the eastern edge of the town of Mariposa, taking off from the point where the much-traveled road from Merced to Yosemite Valley leaves that southernmost of the old mining towns. It winds northward across rolling uplands deeply intersected by the canyons of swift rivers, through dozens of busy small cities and villages of today and ghost towns and camps of yesterday, following a fairly direct route through the region where the Golden Age of California unfolded its remarkable history. A few miles before reaching the northern terminus—junction with Highway 89 on its way from Mount Shasta to Lake Tahoe—it climbs over Yuba Pass (elevation 6700 feet) and drops down into Sierra Valley on the eastern side of the Sierra crest. It is the artery of the foothill gold belt. Traversing it from end to end the traveler passes through nine counties—Mariposa, Tuolumne, Calaveras, Amador, El Dorado, Placer, Yuba, Nevada and Sierra—all dotted with historical landmarks and made memorable by the violent impact of the gold rush, its decade of mushroom growth, its brief florescence and rapid decline.

Many lateral roads from the coast and valley cities of California as well as from the Nevada side give convenient access to the Mother Lode Highway. Farthest south, the All Year Highway (140) from Merced to Yosemite Valley, which marks the beginning of Highway 49 at Mariposa, is the easiest means of reaching the world famous wonderland of granite domes, towering cliffs, waterfalls and soaring peaks, hence it is one of the best known of the mountain roads. It enters Yosemite National Park at El Portal and continues its spectacular route through the length of the valley.

Some fifty miles farther north the Mother Lode Highway crosses Highway 120 which comes from Oakdale by way of Knights Ferry and Chinese Camp. It may be seen winding up Priests Grade above Moccasin Creek Power Station. At the top of the grade it proceeds through Big Oak Flat and Groveland and continues through some of the most rugged and magnificent scenery in the whole Sierra, one branch of it dropping rapidly into Yosemite Valley near the granite wall, El Capitan, the other following the Grand Canyon of the Tuolumne, crossing Tuolumne Meadows lying green and lovely at the base of snowy peaks of the High Sierra, and over the crest at Tioga Pass (elevation 9947 feet), the highest of the mountain passes. From the summit it makes a breathtaking drop down Leevining Creek to Mono Lake 3175 feet below.

Ten miles after crossing Highway 120 our Highway 49 reaches Sonora where it meets Highway 108, a popular route into ski country in winter and at all times a much-frequented recreational area. Winding up through magnificent forests and around enormous domes and knobs of granite, it reaches Sonora Summit (elevation 9624 feet) and proceeds down the eastern face of the mountains, meeting U. S. Highway 395 some seventeen miles north of Bridgeport. This road is a convenient approach to the gold belt from the east.

Highway 4, a rather direct road from the San Francisco Bay region, passes through Angels Camp, seventeen miles beyond Sonora, and continues on through Murphys, past the entrance to the Calaveras Big Trees State Park, through Big Meadows and on over the crest at Ebbetts Pass (elevation 8800 feet) down to Markleeville and on to Lake Tahoe.

Highway 8 from Stockton connects with roads leading into our Highway 49 at San Andreas, Mokelumne Hill and Jackson, and at Jackson, too, another main road (88) from Stockton comes in by way of Ione and continues over the mountains at Kit Carson Pass, where Frémont entered California in 1844.

The next lateral giving access to the Mother Lode Highway is Highway 16 from Sacramento, which comes in between Drytown and Plymouth and goes on to Fiddletown, a short and interesting excursion into the past.

Somewhat farther north, Highway 49 crosses U. S. Highway 50 which carries an enormous volume of traffic from San Francisco, through Oakland, Stockton, Sacramento and Placerville, over Echo Pass (elevation 7394 feet), around the south end of Lake Tahoe, and on through Carson City, Nevada, to the east.

A second great United States Highway (40) which crosses the Sacramento Valley by way of Vacaville and Davis goes through Sacramento and crosses our highway at Auburn. Perhaps the chief artery across the Sierra Nevada, it goes over the Donner Summit (elevation 7113 feet) to Truckee and Reno on its way across Nevada and on to the eastern coast.

At Grass Valley the last of the important laterals crosses the Mother Lode Highway. This is Highway 20 which begins at Ukiah on the Redwood Highway, skirts Clear Lake and traverses the Sacramento Valley by way of the Sutter Buttes and Marysville, goes on to Grass Valley and Nevada City whence it proceeds east and joins U. S. 40 somewhat west of the Donner Summit.

Scores of lesser roads branch from these well traveled highways inviting the traveler to explore one canyon after another of the network of rivers, the gently inclined slopes that remain as watersheds between the canyons, the lakes and forests, and the hundreds of hamlets and almost deserted sites where once flourished the feverish activity of the quest for gold.

No region in the United States has accumulated a richer or more extensive tradition than the western slope of the Sierra from Yosemite to the Yuba River. It was inevitable that a mass migration of adventurous men, young for the most part, and willing to undergo any hardships that might lead to sudden wealth, should create a romantic tradition. Most of them were Americans, but by no means all, for the news of the discovery traveled fast and from all over the world men converged on the gold fields. Mexicans came early and South Americans followed. Chinese and Australians crossed the Pacific. Argonauts hastened westward from England, Wales, Scotland, Ireland. Cornishmen and Frenchmen jostled Germans and Italians in the rush for the diggings. Each of these nationalities left some mark, large or small, on the Mother Lode Country, chiefly in the way of names given to camps, and river bars as well as larger geographical features. Indeed the very name Mother Lode is a heritage from the Mexican miners who were among the earliest comers. Their native province in Mexico was Sonora, a rich mining district with veins of gold-bearing quartz similar to the great dominant veins that extend for about seventy miles in a fairly straight line from Mariposa north to Plymouth. The Sonorian vein was known as the *Veta Madre* and the Mexicans applied the name to what they believed to be the source of the rich placers in the new field. These Sonorians were inspired miners. Their uncanny sense of where to look for gold and their skill and experience in unearthing it were responsible for the location of some of the best placers and quartz mines of the early days.

It is strange that these Mexicans left so few traces in the Mother Lode Country. A few vestiges of their buildings, a few place names remain—notably Sonora, originally Sonoran Camp, one of their first diggings—but the mark they made is largely obliterated. Easy-going people, they vanished before the more vigorous, aggressive and infinitely more numerous Americans, Europeans and Chinese who soon overran the country. But they left as witness of their brief sojourn the name they gave the dominant vein—a name that soon came to designate the whole region of the southern mines, and then to embrace the entire gold belt from Mariposa to Downieville.

The romantic tradition of the gold country was of course enormously augmented by the literary activities of the two popular writers, Bret Harte and Mark Twain. As a matter of fact, neither of these builders of the tradition spent a great deal of time at the mines, and Bret Harte, at least, leaned very heavily on the chronicles of others, but they both possessed in large measure the gift of painting vivid word pictures and creating convincing and appealing characters. Consequently Mark Twain's *Jumping Frog of Calaveras County* and Bret Harte's *Outcasts of Poker Flat, Tennessee's Pardner,* and dozens of others are known all over the world. As surely as England has its Hardy country, California has its well defined, if somewhat mythical, Mark Twain-Bret Harte country. Literary pilgrimages are made to the Mark Twain Cabin on Jackass Hill near Angels Camp. This is a replica of the original cabin, destroyed by fire except for the still usable chimneyplace, in which Mark Twain spent some five months with the Gillis brothers and probably wrote part at least of *The Jumping Frog.* And the pilgrimage goes on to Second Garotte, a village near Groveland on Highway 20, to

another small frame house which *Tennessee* and his *Pardner* are said to have inhabited before Bret Harte immortalized them.

The foothill gold belt, however, was not in want of any amplification of its charm. It is so bountifully endowed with natural beauty and with pleasantness of climate as to be one of the most fortunate regions of California. The whole effect of the country is comfortable and pleasing. It is none the less interesting for the fact that throughout its two-hundred-mile length it is repeatedly scarred as a result of all the diverse methods of gold mining ever devised—naked rocks exposed by surface placers, miles of gravel hills left behind by dredges, mountains of tailings from the quartz mines, and the monstrous cavities gouged out by the giant force of hydraulic mining.

A century ago this virgin western slope of the Sierra must have appeared a paradise to the exhausted travelers who had braved the hazards of the journey overland. The long gentle decline from the crest to the level floor of the wide valley below promised easy progress compared with the perilous eastern front they had surmounted. And though the promise was not always fulfilled and the descent was obstructed with terrific difficulties—lakes, cliffs, granite domes and cruelly deep canyons—the pine forests with their carpets of needles, the sheltered coves and flowery meadows must have seemed, as they do today, unequaled places in which to find rest.

Evidences that many of the pioneers did settle into homes in this favored region remain in the numerous dwellings which date back to the earliest days. Many of them are in ruins, but a surprising number are actually still in use. Here and there an old house stands in an old-fashioned garden, overhung by ancient rosebushes grown, perhaps, from slips brought from distant eastern homes to grace the new dwelling. These decrepit homesteads with their enormous old fruit trees create an appearance of settled human occupation, adding notably to the charm of the mining region which in so many places is marked by melancholy evidences of a life that was born, flourished and declined in a few brief decades.

Fur trappers who had been working through the Rocky Mountains were the first Americans to look westward toward the desert and mountain barriers that shut California away from the eastern United States. They blazed all the trails across the continent which were later followed by explorers, settlers, and forty-niners and later by railroad builders and even the makers of modern highways.

Jedediah Strong Smith, greatest of the pathfinders, was the first American to discover the beauties of the western slope of the Sierra. This was in 1827, and it is a curious fact that the first epochmaking crossing of the range, which revealed the beauties as well as the desperate perils involved in the undertaking, was from west to east.

Starting in August of 1826 Smith and a small party of adventurers had succeeded in crossing the southwestern wilderness that lay between Salt Lake and the Pacific Coast. From Indians in the upper reaches of the Columbia River among whom they had spent the previous winter, they had heard fascinating whispers of a great expanse of valley land behind mountain barriers. These rumors had created an ambition in the minds of Smith and certain of his comrades to open this territory to American expansion. Accordingly they had set out over a difficult route from Salt Lake to the Colorado River, probably by way of St. George and the Virgin River. From the Colorado they made their perilous way through the Mojave Desert, crossed the San Bernardino Mountains and arrived on November 27th at San Gabriel, where the monks of that rich comfortable mission welcomed them and entertained them for some weeks.

Without passports, the pioneers realized they were subject by Mexican law to arrest if they remained without authorization in California, and accordingly they went to San Diego to request official permission to do a bit of trapping in the lakes and streams. Governor Echeandía, however, summarily refused their plea. To him they appeared a hazard to the security of Mexico, which in the light of later history they and their successors proved to be. The Yankee captains of trading vessels had been welcome for years at the sea coast towns and nobody had considered them a hazard. They came, traded and sailed away. In fact, as Americans have been regarded in the ports of all the world, they were considered a desirable economic asset. But the purposeful strangers who had struggled on weary feet across the deserts and scaled the mountain wall were a different problem, and Governor Echeandía gave them only time to get away.

On January 18, 1827, they left the friendly monks of San Gabriel and withdrew hastily, returning to the desert via Cajon Pass, and made their way into the San Joaquin Valley through one of the passes in the Tehachapi Mountains. Beyond the observation of the Californians they slowed their pace, trapping as they progressed along the eastern foothills, and finally established a camp, probably somewhere on the lower course of the Stanislaus River. From there they made scouting forays up the valley, perhaps as far as the American River.

In the spring Captain Smith and two companions undertook the formidable task of crossing the Sierra Nevada. It required eight days of bitter struggle, but they did succeed in ascending the western slope and conquering the summit, probably somewhat south of Sonora Pass, whence they descended and followed the West Walker River to the Nevada desert and on to their headquarters near Salt Lake.

In 1833 Joseph Reddeford Walker led a party westward over the Sierra and down to the valley, in all likelihood, along the divide between the Merced and Tuolumne Rivers. The records indicate that some of the men of this party may have come upon Yosemite as well as one or another or the groves of giant sequoias.

The explorations of these first of the Mountain Men were followed by those of the fur traders, notably the Patties and Ewing Young. And in the wake of the traders came settlers, inspired by the reports of the pioneers to seek new homes in the West. The Swiss empire-builder John August Sutter, who had come to San Francisco in 1839 full of dreams which were to come true in the heart of the Sacramento Valley, was completely established before 1843 in his New Helvetia, the 49,000 acres of land granted to him by the Mexican government. His men were ranging around in the valleys on the western slope of the Sierra considerably before the golden chapter of California history opened on the American River in 1848.

The first settlers to enter California by crossing the Sierra were those who made up the Bidwell-Bartleson party in 1841. These adventurers were made of stern stuff to survive the perils of the route they followed up the eastern escarpment and over the summit at a point somewhere near Sonora Pass. Their last ox had been killed and eaten and they were almost at the end of their strength when they finally found themselves over the crest. And the descent at this point was if possible more difficult than the climb up the eastern face. Exhausted and almost starving, they made their way over masses of granite, around lakes, and up and down canyons of appalling depth and steepness. Probably they followed the watershed between the South Fork of the Stanislaus and the North Fork of the Tuolumne, and the temporary camp they set up at the end of the ordeal was not far from Knights Ferry on the Middle Fork of the Stanislaus.

Fortunately the difficulties surmounted by these earliest explorers did not discourage new attemps to overcome the barriers. In 1843-44 John C. Frémont was leading a party authorized by the American government on an exploration of the far west. Late in 1843 he left Oregon and set out to the southeast with the purpose of returning to St. Louis. Somewhere along the Carson River he made a sudden change in his plan and decided to make a winter crossing of the Sierra into California. Early in February he stopped near Markleeville and from there made his way up the mountains reaching the summit at Kit Carson Pass, later so named in honor of the invincible guide who led Frémont's party through the pass. This route, known by the name Kit Carson Emigrant Trail, was one of the most commonly traveled of the roads of the pioneers.

Later in 1844 a group of thirty-six persons, led by Andrew Kelsey who had been a member of the Bidwell-Bartleson party, crossed the Sierra, and a still larger group known as the Stephens-Murphy party had the distinction of being the first emigrants to bring wagons all the way from Missouri to California. These parties entered over much the same route as that followed over the Donner Summit today by U. S. Highway 40. That route, known then as the California Trail was commonly followed by later settlers. It was the one chosen by the ill-starred Donner Party which met disaster in the winter of 1846-47.

Accounts of that terrible mountain tragedy did nothing to turn aside the flood of western expansion which was now gaining rapidly in volume. And so it was that considerably before the hordes of Argonauts arrived to spread over the foothills like a swarm of locusts, scattered Americans were at home in the region. Americans had looked with wonder into the great canyons of most of the Sierran rivers and had discovered many of the distinctive features that set the western slope of the Sierra Nevada apart from all the rest of the world.

They had discovered some of the groups of giant sequoias, the most massive as well as the most magnificent trees in existence. Oldest of all living things, they have grown in their isolated groups for as many as three thousand years. Some of them have attained a height of three hundred feet, and the trunks of the biggest specimens are as much as thirty-five feet in diameter. Thirty-two separate groves of these forest giants are scattered between Tulare and Placer Counties. Although fossil remains indicate that in long past ages they inhabited much of the northern hemisphere, this western flank of the Sierra is the only place in the world that they exist today.

A century ago the discoverer of a group of these survivors of a

vanished age could not know how rare a find he had made. He had seen that many of the natural features of California were on a huge scale—and here was another. But today's traveler in the Mother Lode Country, knowing the extreme antiquity of the *Sequoia gigantea*, which is even more astonishing than its size and beauty, will certainly wish to visit one or another of the groves. Calaveras Big Trees State Park, northernmost of the larger groves, is easily accessible from the Mother Lode Highway. At Angels Camp, Highway 4 offers a direct route through Murphys, one of the best preserved of the old mining towns. Twenty miles northeast of Murphys the grove lies south of the road close to the North Fork of the Stanislaus River. At any season it is a memorable sight. In spring when the sturdy lower growth of dogwood is in blossom it is incredibly beautiful.

And this is only one of the dozens of byways that tempt the traveler to turn aside for a time from the pleasant winding artery of the Sierra Gold Belt and explore more deeply into the foothill and mountain country. Every branching road and trail offers some scene of natural beauty, some landmark of historical significance, some relic of the colorful past or evidence of the manifold activity of today.

FIG. 1.   Old covered bridge at Bridgeport spanning the North Fork of the Yuba River. Still in use. *Photo by Olaf P. Jenkins.*

FIG. 2.   Winter view from Sierra City on Highway 49 toward the pretertiary divide. *Photo by Olaf P. Jenkins.*

THE DISCOVERY OF GOLD IN CALIFORNIA

By Donald C. Cutter

When James Wilson Marshall found gold in the tailrace of Sutter's Mill on January 24, 1848, he was not the first to come across this much sought mineral in California. As early as 1816, there were reports of gold in the Spanish province of California. Reports and rumors of gold persisted, but it was not until 1842 that there was a real gold rush in the future Golden State. Either late in 1841 or early in 1842, Francisco Lopez, majordomo of the San Fernando Rancho, and a companion were in search of some stray cattle in the mountains near the ranch. Becoming tired they dismounted to rest in San Feliciano Canyon. Here Lopez whipped out his knife to dig some wild onions to eat and in the earth clinging to them he found particles of what appeared to him to be gold. Using his knife he continued to mine in the vicinity and found additional alluvial gold deposits. Following this gold find came the first rush in California history. Californians left the monotony of their daily life and went to this canyon located thirty-five miles northeast of the Pueblo of Los Angeles. Although they used the crudest of methods and were without nearby water to pan their gold, some of the miners succeeded in making their operations profitable. The first gold-seekers at the Los Angeles placers were the local residents, but within the year men of greater mining experience were imported from Sonora. These miners introduced into California the method which became known as dry washing to extract the gold. As a method of mining it was simple, crude and inefficient, but it had the advantage of being inexpensive. After the pay dirt was dug, it was sun dried on a large canvas and then pulverized into dust. The next operation was to throw the dirt by the panful into the air in order to allow the wind to blow away the lighter elements and to let the gold dust fall back into the pan. Thus the old agricultural procedure of winnowing was the first method used extensively in California mining; for not only was it used in the Los Angeles area, but also it was introduced by many of these same Sonorans into the mines of the Sierra Nevada after 1848.

One wonders why this gold find was not more generally known, especially since the estimates of the productiveness of the placers were considerable. William Heath Davis, an early pioneer, estimated that $80,000 to $100,000 in gold was taken from the mines in the first two years. Abel Stearns, a resident of Los Angeles, estimated that $6000 to $8000 a year was extracted prior to 1847. Hubert Howe Bancroft, the historian of California, states that by December 1843, 2000 ounces had been taken, valued at $38,000. These however are merely estimates of production. As a matter of record, the first California gold dust sent to a United States Mint belonged to the aforementioned Don Abel Stearns. On July 8, 1843 his package of 18.34 ounces of placer gold was deposited in the Philadelphia mint by Alfred Robinson. The gold had been transported around the Horn and at the mint brought somewhat over $19 an ounce. It cannot be said that the United States Government was not officially informed of the existence of gold in California, for Thomas O. Larkin as vice-consul at Monterey notified Secretary of State James Buchanan of the fact in an official communication of March 1846. In view of these circumstances, what were the reasons for the lack of publicity of this early uncovering of gold? Doubtless they are a combination of the following: the small amount of gold was soon exhausted; inadequate mining processes and difficulty of extraction made gold mining economically profitable in the long run only to those with previous mining experience; the Mexicans had inherited the Spanish ideas of mercantilism in pursuit of which policy trade and communication with foreign nations were discouraged and consequently the possibility of publicity was lessened; and in general, the Mexican authorities were not favorably inclined to increased immigration into California.

It is obvious that James Marshall was not the first to find gold in California, and in justice to Francisco Lopez, Marshall ought not to be so credited. Nevertheless it was this New Jersey carpenter, in the employ of John Sutter, who made the *effective* discovery which electrified the world, altered the course of western history, greatly accelerated the development of California, and had national and international ramifications.

FIG. 1. Sutter's mill as it stood soon after its abandonment. This picture was probably taken in 1853. The man in the foreground is supposed to be James Marshall.

Fig. 2. Air photo of Coloma Valley looking north. Town of Coloma is west of the bridge in the center of the panorama. *Photo by courtesy of National Park Service.*

For years, John Sutter, grantee and almost feudal baron of a large Mexican grant in the vicinity of present day Sacramento, desired to provide a supply of lumber for his own use and for sale. Consequently he provided for the establishment of two mills, a sawmill at Coloma and a gristmill at Natoma. The latter mill was to use the products of the former in its construction. In August 1847, Sutter signed a contract with Marshall which provided that Marshall should erect and operate the mill and that Sutter should supply the labor, tools, supplies and equipment. After they had determined the location for the proposed mill on the South Fork of the American River, in a small valley which was later to be called Coloma, they built two cabins, one to house the workers and the other the boss—Marshall. The work of construction of the mill advanced quite rapidly after its commencement in September. Laborers, Indians, Mormons and others were employed and the work on the mill was almost finished by January of the following year (1848). This early completion was due in considerable measure to the industry and abilities of the Mormon workers who had been recently discharged from the Mormon Battalion.

The story of this group of soldiers and their part in the discovery of gold in California is of considerable interest. The battalion, about 500 strong, volunteered for service in the United States Army for the Mexican War. Besides desiring to aid their country, the Saints enlisted in order to become the advance guard of the Mormon westward migration. The termination of their one year enlistments found a considerable portion of the original group in Southern California, after having opened a wagon road to the West. Some of the group, about 81 in number, re-enlisted for an additional year of service. The remainder, some 240, were released after exemplary service. By this time the Battalion had been informed that the new headquarters for the faith was to be in Utah, and they began to head for that destination. The soldiers were not, however, the only Mormons in the Golden State at the time, for on July 31, 1846, a group of homeseekers had arrived aboard the sailing ship *Brooklyn* led by Sam Brannan as presiding elder. Late in 1847, this same Brannan met the homeward bound group of ex-soldiers at Tahoe Basin. There he urged the men to remain in California until the following spring since it was already September. Brannan's entreaties were of no avail but a bundle of letters and an epistle from Brigham Young, which arrived the following day, changed the minds of many. In the epistle they were advised by their leader to remain in California until they had outfitted themselves, unless their presence in Utah was essential. Thereupon most of the group turned back and sought employment in California. About 40 of the young ex-soldiers found work with John Sutter, some being sent to Natoma, some to Coloma, and others remaining to work at Sutter's Fort at New Helvetia. Probably about nine of the Mormons were assigned to Marshall at Coloma, this group entering into a contract with Sutter whereby they agreed to remain in his employ until the completion of

work on the sawmill. One of the Mormons, Henry Bigler, kept a diary from which historians have drawn heavily in determining the details of the discovery and the actual date thereof as January 24, 1848. In spite of the discovery of gold the Mormons completed the provisions of their contract with Sutter and engaged in mining only when they were off duty at the mill. By March 11th, the work on the sawmill was finished and it was in operation. Presently the Mormons terminated their contract with Sutter, were paid off at about $1.50 per day for work at the mill, and set about digging gold on a full time basis at Mormon Island near the confluence of the South and Main Forks of the American River. Here many of the Saints joined in the enterprise, working the area until June of the same year, at which time the members of the Battalion decided to leave for the home in Utah which they had not yet seen. In July, forty-five of them united and left the easy money of California for the alkaline plains of Salt Lake Valley, because of their attachment to the faith. This marked the first return of miners from the gold fields, and was a preview of the role that California would play in the filling in of the West.

Just as the date of the discovery has been a subject of discussion, the accounts of the events leading up to Marshall's find and his actions thereafter conflict in different narratives. The main facts however are in accord. The sawmill constructed by Marshall was operated by diverting the water of the river through a headrace into the forebay of the mill, whence it was directed to the waterwheel, flowed under the length of the mill and escaped back into the river through a tailrace. It was determined by test in December 1847, that the mill foundations had been set too low and therefore the water did not escape sufficiently into the tailrace. This necessitated the deepening and widening of the race to expedite the run-off of the water.

Leaving the mill in the same month, Marshall ordered that this work should be accomplished in his absence. Upon his return to the mill, Marshall found that his orders had been carried out, but the race was still not sufficiently deep. Additional excavation was done during the daytime, and at night the gates of the forebay were opened and the running water assisted the work by clearing away the loose dirt. Boulders were blasted out and the decomposed granite was being dug out manually by both the Indian laborers and the Mormons. On the morning of January 24th, when Marshall was making one of his frequent inspections of the tailrace, something glittering caught his eye. There, resting in a shallow depth of water, was a yellow flake of what appeared to be metal. Testing its malleability, he became hopeful; he picked up some more flakes, placed them in the crown of his hat and made his way to where the men were working. The Mormons shared Marshall's interest and several elementary tests were made, by which the group could not disprove the possibility that the metal was gold. Work on the mill was halted temporarily while all went to the tailrace to pick up these available flakes of metal. Use of the fingers alone was found to be exceedingly difficult, but the assistance of a knife in gathering gold was discovered to be efficient; thus the knife was the first implement used in mining at Coloma as well as at the Los Angeles placers. By this knife method several ounces of gold were collected. Further tests were given the metal, all of which were favorable; but in order to make certain, Marshall decided to depart for Sutter's Fort for a conference with his partner-boss. More scientific tests were applied there, proving beyond a reasonable doubt the authenticity of the find.

The plans of Sutter and Marshall to keep the discovery quiet came to naught, for the secret of gold could not be kept. The ex-soldiers at the Coloma millsite confided the secret to their associates at Natoma. Charles Bennett, sent by Sutter to Monterey to secure a grant of the Coloma area from Governor Mason, could not restrain himself from showing the gold in Benicia and San Francisco. Upon hearing of gold, Sam Brannan, the Mormon elder, could not curb his curiosity and visited Sacramento. Upon his return to San Francisco he did not hesitate to proclaim the discovery. Even Sutter, who most wanted the secret maintained, confided the news to General Vallejo. The first published announcement of the discovery of gold was made on March 15, 1848, in the San Francisco weekly newspaper *The Californian,* and no longer could the discovery be withheld from the whole world.

While in San Francisco, Sutter's agent, Charles Bennett, sought the advice of an ex-Georgia miner, Isaac Humphrey, and showed him the gold. The miner lost very little time in getting to the location of the discovery and became the first of many professional miners in the gold fields. Among other things he is credited with having introduced machinery when, on March 9, 1848, two days after his arrival, he made use of the rocker for the first time in California. He had the distinction of being the first professional only by the space of a few days, for a French Canadian backwoodsman soon arrived who had had previous mining experience in Sonora. He was Jean Baptiste Ruelle, called by all simply Baptiste. He and Humphrey were a great help to the many greenhorns, who were arriving in increasing numbers. These mining men, augmented by the arrival of some Sonorans from the Los Angeles placers, were the authorities on gold mining, the Sonoran miners being the vanguard of thousands of foreigners to be lured by California's wealth.

The crude method of pen-knife and butcher-knife mining soon gave way to more adequate methods of placer mining. The *batea,* or dish shaped Indian basket, the iron gold pan, and the cradle, which were used to expedite the process of separation of gold and sediment, were soon in evidence. The cradle (or rocker as it was often called) proved to be inefficient because of the loss of many of the small particles, and was soon improved. The new development was the Long Tom, an elongated cradle in which transverse cleats arrested these small gold particles. Soon, however, the Long Tom was superseded by sluices of various types.

Booming or gouging was the next innovation in mining technique. This consisted of merely letting water do the work of clearing away the sediment. A dam was built, and the water diverted through the area which was being mined; the water carried the lighter elements downstream, leaving the gold-bearing ore easily accessible to be worked by one of the other methods of placer mining. The success of this procedure soon brought about the introduction of hydraulic mining—the use of water under pressure. It is claimed that water was used in this manner at Yankee Jim's in 1852. Perhaps more definite is the assertion that in the same year Anthony Chabot used the hydraulic method without a nozzle at Buckeye Hill, near Nevada City. Hydraulic mining seems to have been a California innovation, and was first employed, complete with the nozzle which is generally associated with this type of mining, in 1853.

The idea of dredging gold was common, but early attempts resulted in failure. Characteristic is the example of an operation on the Yuba River in 1853 in which the dredge sank almost immediately. Despite many subsequent dredging endeavors, it was not until 1898 that the first real success was achieved. This was accomplished with a bucket elevator dredge used on the Feather River near Oroville.

The easily worked alluvial deposits of gold extracted by the early miners made mining look simple, and this fact added to the many stories of fabulous wealth lured thousands of men to the gold fields of California. Nevertheless the discovery of new placers did not await their coming. Not long after Marshall's discovery, John Bidwell, grantee of Rancho Chico, visited the Coloma site. Returning home to his rancho, he found gold at what became known as Bidwell's Bar on the Feather River. P. B. Reading also visited the discovery site, became convinced that there were similar indications on his land, and on his return to his home found some deposits on Clear Creek, which he worked with Indian labor. Success on Clear Creek led Reading to further finds on Trinity River, just as success on the Feather River stimulated discoveries on the Yuba. Before the end of 1848, finds of gold had become numerous and the gold area extended from the Tuolumne on the south to the Trinity on the north.

Men of mining experience sought the source vein or veins from which the alluvial deposits originated. The first such vein, which was of gold quartz, was discovered on Colonel John C. Frémont's Mariposa grant in August 1849. It was probably not until 1850 or 1851, that the term Mother Lode was first applied. At that time it was used to designate a vein worked at Nashville, twelve miles south of Placerville.

In the years following '48 and '49, more and more areas were opened and worked, and the gold production of California was immense. The significance of these discoveries, of the resulting rushes, and of the partial abandonment of the area is enormous. Thousands of men came by wagon, by ship and even by foot to become rich in the Golden State. Most of them desired to return home after striking it rich. Some did, but many remained in California to populate the new American acquisition. As a result of the gold rush, California became a state without going through the usual territorial status, since its population was sufficient for its entry into the union on equal terms with the other states. The nature of prospecting made exploration of the state complete and rapid, most portions being inspected in the hope of finding gold. The results of the influx of forty-niners caused the State to go through a turbulent, and oftentimes lawless, period of growing pains, but a period from which it emerged the most important western state.

The California gold rush stimulated strikes in all parts of the world. Marshall's discovery was the direct stimulus for the important New South Wales find of 1851 and the resulting rush. In the general search for gold, a strike was made on the Fraser River in western Canada. This rush drew many fortune hunters. In 1859-60, the silver bonanza of the Comstock Lode was made by prospectors seeking gold. Additional gold fields were discovered in Colorado in 1859, and many of the miners were Californians. These gold rushes and subsequent strikes drew men away from California in considerable numbers, but began the process of filling the gaps of settlement between the Middle and Far West. Thus the discovery of gold not only hastened the development of one state, but also that of the whole West, either directly or indirectly.

The economic consequences and significance of the discovery of gold are equally great but harder to determine. Increased production in the United States, followed by increased foreign production resulting from the California gold rush, caused an increase of money in circulation. By 1865 in California alone $750,000,000 in gold had been mined, and this figure is considered a conservative estimate. In spite of the heavy increase of circulating gold, the much-feared serious inflation, which was predicted by economists, failed to materialize. True, in California, at the source of gold and where commodities were scarce, initial inflation was tremendous; but world inflation as a result of the California gold rush, and its successors, was slight. Estimates of inflation range from 5 percent to 15 percent. This low figure is explained by an existing world scarcity of money caused in part by increasing world population.

Other important results of the gold rush were that it opened the era of modern mining; hastened the colonization of the West and the suppression and partial elimination of the Indian; accelerated the expansion of the agricultural frontier by the need for a food supply in the gold area; and speeded the linking of the East and West. The California rush has the distinction of being the first modern international gold rush, since all previous gold rushes in modern times were exclusive, under the theory of mercantilism. Since subsequent rushes were, for the most part, international in character, a fresh distribution of population was produced not only in the United States but also in many portions of the world. This redistribution of population with its resulting problems together with the general increase of money put into circulation, is the primary significance to the world of Marshall's discovery.

BIBLIOGRAPHY

BAILEY, PAUL D., Sam Brannan and the Mormons: Westernlore Press, 187 pp., Los Angeles, 1943.

BANCROFT, HUBERT H., History of California: A. L. Bancroft and Co. and The History Co., 7 vols., San Francisco, 1884-1890.

BEKEART, PHILLIP B., James W. Marshall, discoverer of gold: Soc. California Pioneers Quarterly, vol. 1, no. 3, pp. 3-43, San Francisco, September 1924.

BUFFUM, E. GOULD, Six months in the gold mines: Richard Bentley, 244 pp., London, 1850.

CENDRARS, BLAISE, Sutters gold: Harper and Bros., 179 pp., New York and London, 1926. Translated from the French by Henry L. Stuart.

CLELAND, ROBERT G., A history of California, the American period: The MacMillan Co., 512 pp., New York, 1922.

COY, OWEN C., Gold days: Powell Pub. Co., 381 pp., Los Angeles, 1929 (1934).

DANA, JULIAN, Sutter of California: Halcyon Press (Blue Ribbon Books, Inc.), 413 pp., New York, 1934.

HULBERT, ARCHER B., Forty-niners: Little, Brown and Co., 340 pp., Boston, 1931.

HUNT, ROCKWELL D., California the golden: Silver, Burdett and Co., 362 pp., New York and Boston, 1911.

PAUL, RODMAN W., California gold: Harvard Univ. Press, 380 pp., Cambridge, Mass., 1947.

QUIETT, GLENN C., Pay dirt, a panorama of American gold rushes: D. Appleton-Century Co., Inc., 506 pp., New York and London, 1936.

RICKARD, THOMAS A., The discovery of gold in California: University of California Chronicle, vol. 30, no. 2, pp. 141-169, Berkeley, 1928.

RICKARD, THOMAS A., A history of American mining: D. Appleton-Century Co., Inc., New York and London, 1932.

ROBERTS, BRIGHAM H., The Mormon battalion: Deseret News, 96 pp., Salt Lake City, 1919.

WHITE, STEWART EDWARD, The forty-niners: Yale Univ. Press, 273 pp., New Haven, 1918.

FIG. 1.   Omega hydraulic mine; the large water pipe supplied the "giants" or hose nozzles. *Photo by Olaf P. Jenkins.*

FIG. 3.   View southwest toward Blue Tent ditch, a typical carrier of water supplying the hydraulic diggings. *Photo by Olaf P. Jenkins.*

FIG. 2.   Depot Hill hydraulic mine near Camptonville.

FIG. 4.   View southwest toward placer mine half a mile east of Downieville.

HISTORY OF PLACER MINING FOR GOLD IN CALIFORNIA

By Charles V. Averill

Methods for the recovery of gold even today depend largely on the high specific gravity of that metal. A particle of gold of a certain size is so much heavier than a particle of associated rock of the same or even larger size, that a current of water washes the particles of dirt and rock away and leaves the gold behind. At Sutter's sawmill, water turned through the ditch to operate the water wheel washed away the dirt and gravel and left the bright flakes of gold. These were caught on the rough bottom of one of the ditches where Marshall found them.

The earliest efforts to recover gold, after Marshall's discovery, were directed toward those places where flakes and nuggets of gold had been concentrated on rough bedrock and in crevices by the natural flow of the streams. Small tools were used to dig in the crevices and to pick up the flakes of gold. Soon the miner's pan came into use. An ordinary frying pan can be used to concentrate gold providing it is free of grease, but the familiar miner's pan with gently sloping sides is more efficient. It is a simple device for washing away the lighter dirt and fine gravel, and concentrating the heavy gold in the bottom of the pan. The capacity of the pan is so limited that gravel very rich in gold is needed to pay by this method. A skilled operator is able to pan less than one cubic yard of gravel during a day's work. The batea is a wooden version of the miner's pan that was introduced into California at a very early date by Mexican miners.

Rockers or cradles and sluice boxes were the next devices used by the early-day miners. The rocker is a crude concentrating machine made of wood that combines the shaking motion of the pan with some of the features of the sluice. Riffles or obstructions are placed across the bottom to catch the heavy flakes of gold. The dirt and gravel are washed over the tops of the riffles. With the rocker, both the gravel and the water are introduced by hand. With the sluice, the water flows by gravity, but the gravel is shoveled in by hand. The miner is able to wash several cubic yards per day—still a small amount of gravel. By 1860, gravel that would pay to work by these methods was getting hard to find, and production of gold declined.

In the meantime the hydraulic method of mining was developed. Great jets of water were directed against banks of gravel hundreds of feet in height. Some of the jets of water were 9 inches in diameter as they left the nozzles. After the proper ditches and pipe lines had been installed, thousands of cubic yards of gravel could be washed without hand labor. The gold was recovered in riffle-sluices, and quicksilver was usually added to aid in its recovery. The debris deposited in streams by hydraulic miners became so objectionable to agricultural interests that the method was stopped by injunction in 1884, and placer production dropped to a very low level.

Evidence of hydraulic mining in the form of old gravel banks may be seen on Highway 49 at Mokelumne Hill in Calaveras County and near Camptonville in Yuba County near the Sierra County line. The Depot Hill mine near Camptonville has been worked quite recently. The Bullard Bar dam of the Pacific Gas and Electric Company is available for the storage of tailings; hence this mine can be operated legally at the present time. Other dams that were constructed primarily for the purpose of restraining such tailings are located on the North Fork American River about two miles above its confluence with Middle Fork American River near Auburn, and on the Yuba River about 1½ miles above its confluence with Deer Creek near Smartsville.

Some of the largest hydraulic mines ever operated are a few miles east of North San Juan. Leaving Highway 49 at this point, one may travel for 15 miles practically along the course of an ancient river channel in which gold-bearing gravel was deposited many millions of years ago to a depth of about 500 feet. The climate was semi-tropical at that time, and the elevation was much lower. The region has been raised by tilting so that the bed of the ancient river now occupies the top of a high ridge. The largest mine was the Malakoff at North Bloomfield, and it was the injunction against this mine in 1884 that practically put a stop to hydraulic mining in this region.

The lode mines with their quartz veins and stamp mills took over the major output of gold, and the production curve rises gradually until about 1900 when connected-bucket dredges were introduced and made the curve rise a little faster. These great machines contain a continuous chain of buckets for digging the gravel and taking it aboard the floating barge. Such a chain of buckets and the support for it (the ladder) may weigh 1,000 tons. The entire outfit including the digging machinery and the equipment for washing out the gold may weigh 3,750 tons. Riffle sluices and quicksilver are still used to recover the gold on the dredges, but sluices are gradually being replaced by jigs, which are mechanical devices for concentrating the gold. The dragline type of dredge is a later development that was introduced in the 1930's. The heavy digging equipment is an ordinary dragline excavator that travels on the bank. The floating barge carries only the screen, equipment for concentrating the gold, and the tailing-stacker. Placer gravel is handled so cheaply on these dredges that gravel running 10 cents to 20 cents per cubic yard can be mined at a profit.

Inflation following World War I stopped the rising trend of gold production, and it declined until the early 1930's, when the increase in price from $20.67 to $35 per fine ounce caused production to rise until 1940. In October 1942 Limitation Order L-208 of the War Production Board stopped all gold mining with few exceptions. This caused great damage to California mines in the form of flooded and caved workings, and gold production is now at a very low level. It cannot be expected to rise very fast under present conditions of high costs of labor and supplies, unless a way can be found so that the miner will receive more than $35 per fine ounce for his gold. The price is higher than this in many countries today.

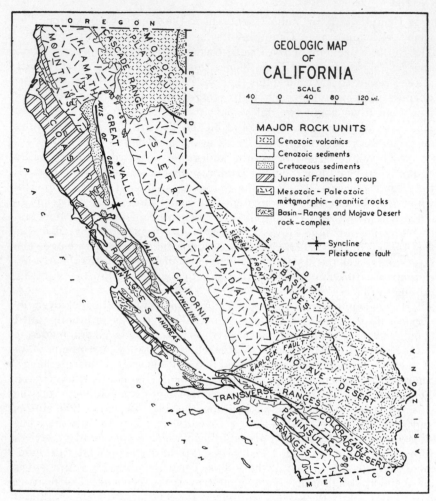

FIG. 5.   Geologic map of California showing major rock units. *Reprinted from*
California Div. Mines Rept. 40, pl. 8.

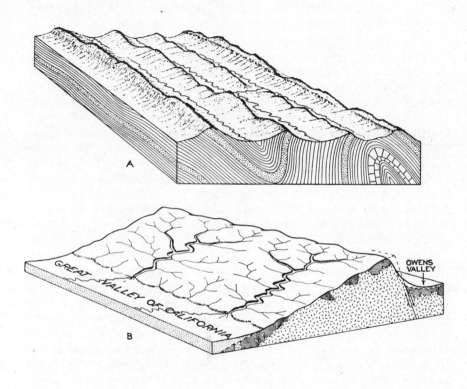

FIG. 6.   *A*, Block diagram illustrating Cretaceous Sierra Nevada topography. The
upturned edges of bedrock controlled the drainage pattern, which was later
inherited by streams of the early Eocene period. *After Matthes, U. S. Geol.*
Survey, Prof. Paper 160, 1930.

B, Block diagram to show tilting of the Sierra Nevada and its effect on stream
cutting. Erosion, prior to the tilting, planed down the surface and exposed
the granite, leaving only occasional fragments of the intruded metamorphic
rock-bodies as roof pendants. The streams, at the point where they leave
their mountain canyons and enter the Great Valley, form alluvial fans.
After Matthes, U. S. Geol. Survey Prof. Paper 160, 1930.

SIERRA NEVADA PROVINCE

By OLAF P. JENKINS

The dominant mountain range of California, the Sierra Nevada, stands as a single and magnificent natural province, over 350 miles long by 60 miles wide. Its eastern rugged wall was a challenge to early explorers; its western wooded slope, a revelation to immigrants who could see from its heights the fertile flat lands of the Great Valley and the Coast Ranges beyond. The deep canyons, waterfalls, and Big Trees from the earliest days were an invitation to tourists from all over the world. Fine timber and water power, summer pasture for stock, playgrounds in both summer and winter—all have made the Sierra Nevada a huge natural resort and at the same time a useful garden spot unsurpassed in the world. All these features and resources have nearly overshadowed its vast mineral wealth, which was by no means exhausted by the excited efforts of the early gold miners.

To describe this fine mountain province or to appreciate its characteristic features, an understanding must be gained of how it was formed and of what it is composed. Some knowledge of the geologic features involved will also be found useful in understanding how the mineral wealth became unlocked to mining ventures.

The shape and form of the Sierra Nevada is the result of stupendous geologic processes. The mountain range has a definite eastern escarpment, formed by comparatively recent faults or displacements in the earth's crust, which took place after the Sierra was raised to tremendous heights, now over 14,000 feet. This eastern front towers as a saw-toothed, snow-capped wall in sharp contrast with the depressed desert valleys lying 10,000 feet below at its eastern foot. The watershed of the range hugs close to this eastern wall, while the western slope is a gradual descent to the Great Valley of the Sacramento and San Joaquin Rivers. This gradual western slope, however, is dissected and broken laterally by rock-walled canyons of exceeding depth, cut by mountain rivers flowing westward to the Great Valley. The uptilting of the Sierra Nevada was the cause of the enormously accelerated flow of its streams, which resulted in the cutting of canyons to the very core of the mountains. The mineral deposits which lay hidden many thousands of feet in depth were thus exposed to view and to exploitation.

The southern end of the Sierra Nevada bends westward where the Tehachapi Mountains and San Emigdio Range form the terminus of the Great Valley. The southwestern point of the Sierra ends abruptly against the junction of the famous San Andreas and Garlock faults. The southern slope gives way to the Mojave Desert on the south as the eastern escarpment faces desert troughs of the Great Basin.

The northern mountain surface of the Sierra Nevada disappears abruptly under the Modoc lava fields and volcanic Cascade Range which completely cover the older relief and separate it from the Klamath Mountains of the northwest.

The Sierran Gold Belt, traversed by Highway 49, starts on the south at Mariposa which is located well back in the foothills and halfway between the northern and southern limits of the Sierra Nevada province. The highway, like the Mother Lode, runs northwestward to Plymouth, crossing the Merced, Tuolumne, Stanislaus, Mokelumne, and Cosumnes Rivers. From Plymouth, the course of the Mother Lode quartz veins is northward to Placerville and beyond, terminating in the vicinity of Georgetown, a distance of 162 miles from Mariposa by highway.

Highway 49 leaves the Mother Lode at Placerville and continues northwestward to Auburn, first crossing the South Fork, then the North Fork of the American River. It continues northward to the famous mining district of Grass Valley and Nevada City. From there it wanders northeastward through the old hydraulic mining region of the gold-bearing gravels of ancient Tertiary streams, the deposits of which now lie near the tops of ridges, where they and their covering of volcanic flows have been lifted by the uptilt of the Sierra. After crossing the deep canyon of the Middle Fork of the Yuba River, Highway 49 reaches Downieville, an important gold-mining district lying on a direct northern trend of the gold-bearing quartz veins of the rich Alleghany district. These in turn may be a continuation of the Mother Lode from Georgetown. Highway 49 continues from Downieville eastward over the Yuba Summit, ending at the edge of Sierra Valley.

The entire course of Highway 49 and its side roads will take the traveler through many of the principal mines of the Sierran Gold Belt, a total distance of 277 miles. Lying to the west of the Mother Lode is the Foothill Copper-Zinc Belt; west of that is the belt of clays, lignite, and quartz sands of the Ione formation. Limestone deposits occur in places throughout this region; a cement plant at San Andreas boasts of one of the largest kilns in the world. The productive resources of this highly mineralized region include gold, silver, some platinum and even a few diamonds, tungsten, copper, lead, zinc, manganese, chromite, iron, limestone, dolomite, clay, lignite, sand, gravel, slate, and building stone.

FIG. 1.   Aerial view of Tuolumne Table Mountain, a lava flow which occupied a channel cut in an extensive flat surface of andesitic ash. The ash was eroded away leaving the harder lava in relief as a long, sinuous, flat-topped ridge. Occasional remnants of the andesite ash may be seen at the base of Table Mountain in numerous places. The Eocene bedrock surface surrounding Table Mountain was largely exhumed by this erosion.

GEOLOGIC HISTORY OF THE SIERRAN GOLD BELT

By Olaf P. Jenkins

The long chronicle of time recorded on this earth by its rocks and pieced together by geologists to form a standard column of sequences, is well represented in California. Indeed, the rocks of the Sierran Gold Belt, which now have our attention, go a long way toward demonstrating the entire historical section.

Although the very early events of pre-Paleozoic and lower Paleozoic time are indefinite in this part of the State, it is quite possible that during this time of veiled antiquity a mountain range stood where the Sierra Nevada now is located. Presence of such a range would have left little chance for sediments to be deposited and therefore nothing in the way of testimony, since geological testimony of history lies in the deposits which are left behind.

Marine deposited sediments with upper Paleozoic fossil corals and other tropical organic life extend over a wide region in the northern Sierra Nevada and prove the existence of an inland sea during that time. Possibly it was only the western margin of the sea, but its waters certainly swept eastward across the present Great Basin area because more complete sections of these sediments are found to the east in the interior of Nevada and southeastern California. Rocks of Silurian, Devonian, Carboniferous, and Permian periods—representing all of the late portion of the Paleozoic era, permit us to start out definitely with an epi-continental sea as the beginning of our history of the rocks we may encounter along Highway 49.

The soft sands, muds, and marls of this early sea are now changed to the form of very hard quartzites, slates, schists, cherts, limestones, and marble. They are so old and have undergone so many episodes of loading, compression, heating, crumpling, crushing, induration, recrystallization, and infiltration of mineral bearing solutions that it is only by the most skillful field and microscopic study that the origin of these rocks may be interpreted.

There is much evidence that volcanism was present during the broad expanse of the 200 million years which elapsed while these Paleozoic rocks were being laid down in the sea basin. The volcanic rocks which are most in evidence are found in the upper Paleozoic. They are now metamorphosed to greenstones and are so difficult to differentiate from those of the later Mesozoic as to present one of the major problems to geologic study. Fluctuations and movements of the earth's crust caused the sediments of this sea basin to be lifted and submerged several times during its span of existence.

The Mesozoic era which came after the Paleozoic is divided into an early part, the Triassic, followed by the Jurassic, and finally the Cretaceous. In the northern Sierra Nevada the Triassic is well represented by marine sediments, but there is not much to be seen of them along Highway 49. The period of tremendous importance in this region is the Jurassic, and especially the latter part of this period. Volcanic activity was widespread throughout the entire province during upper Jurassic. It may have been an ominous warning of the stupendous mountain-making epoch that concluded the Jurassic and resulted in a folded mountain range, the rocks of which were intruded throughout by a molten granitic magma. Mineralized quartz veins, formed by the filling and enlargement of cracks in the rocks with siliceous material, followed the granitic intrusion represent the end product of this major epoch of disturbance in California. All this took place over 100 million years ago and the rocks of that period which we see exposed today were probably buried then at a depth of at least two miles.

Not all the rocks of the Upper Jurassic, however, are of eruptive origin. There are the Mariposa slates, for example; these are marine in origin. Some non-marine sediments were also deposited during the Jurassic and there are many kinds of igneous intrusions associated with the Upper Jurassic. Into the muds and other rocks of this period (also of the Paleozoic), serpentine rocks bearing chromite were injected. These ultra-basic intrusives antedate the granitic rock intrusions and may have been introduced prior to folding of the sediments.

The episode or episodes of folding present most interesting problems. The whole scheme of affairs on this part of the earth was changed in Upper Jurassic time, because the sea basin of long standing (hundreds of millions of years) was destroyed. The strata were raised above sea level and compressed into a complicated series of folds trending for the most part northwest-southeast. As the granitic magma was intruded, large sections of the earlier rocks disappeared. Perhaps they were assimilated by the granite or pushed aside, or maybe the granite itself was manufactured from the earlier rocks by melting. All we actually know, however, is that where the granite is present now the earlier rocks are gone. In many places the granitic rocks (largely granodiorite) include fragments of earlier rocks as if floating within their firm crystalline structure. At the southern end of the Mother Lode, at Mormon Bar, the earlier rocks give way to granite, and thus the belt of Mother Lode quartz veins is terminated.

The time interval required for the folding of all the sediments of the Paleozoic, Triassic and Jurassic plus the intrusion of granite was geologically not very long. It was a mountain-making epoch of a comparatively short span, all within the upper part of the Upper Jurassic. The cooling, contracting, and releasing of mineral-bearing solutions by the granitic rocks permitted quartz veins to fill the resulting fractures in the rocks and the fractures previously formed by faulting during the folding episode.

All these rocks—Paleozoic sediments, Triassic and Jurassic sediments and volcanics, intrusive basic and ultra-basic rocks, intrusive or

SUMMARY OF GEOLOGIC HISTORY OF SIERRAN GOLD BELT
HISTORY OF THE SOFTER ROCKS ("SUPERJACENT SERIES" WHICH CONTAINS THE PLACERS AND OVERLIES THE "BEDROCK SERIES")

Geologic era	Geologic period		Geologic event	Geologic record	Duration in millions of years	

Cenozoic	Quaternary	Recent	History of man
			   Quartz mining
			     Placer mining
			       Dredging
			         Hydraulic mining
			           Shallow, hand placering
				Historical record
				
				2¼ billion dollars gold produced
						Age

		Pleistocene	Resurrection of ancient channels and old Tertiary surfaces Continued faulting Glaciation Canyon cutting, robbing gold from earlier Eocene channels Uplift and faulting	Physiographic features Rock exposures Gravel deposits	1	1–2
	Tertiary	Pliocene	Continued basic volcanic activity Uplift and faulting Intervolcanic streams Andesitic flows, concealing old surface	Mehrten formation (andesite) -------?-----------	7	8
		Miocene	Andesitic lavas, breccias, ash, mud flows, covering all but the higher peaks and ranges Ash falls, covering surfaces	Valley Springs formation (rhyolite)	12	20
		Oligocene	Rhyolitic ash falls dam streams, covering channels		16	36
		Eocene Paleocene	Deposition of large stream deposits of white quartz gravel (angular and subangular) and placer gold Deposition of Ione clay, lignite, and sand (in part marine) Release of gold from rocks and veins Decay of rocks, formation of deep red soil Semi-tropical weathering	Ancient channels Ione formation Ancient channels Old surfaces Deep red soil	23	60
Mesozoic	Upper Cretaceous		Pirate streams rob east-flowing streams, cutting the Pre-Tertiary Divide and Great Western Divide Tops of gold-bearing veins reached by erosion Deposition of sand and gravel in basin west of Sierra Nevada Erosion and removal of rocks 2 miles thick from top of Sierra	Chico formation Conglomerates, sandstones, and shales many miles in thickness (Great Valley)	35	95
			Profound unconformity			

HISTORY OF THE "BEDROCK SERIES" WHICH CONTAINS THE VEINS

Geologic era	Geologic period	Geologic event	Geologic record	Duration in millions of years

Mesozoic	Upper Jurassic
	
	Lower Jurassic
		Profound unconformity
		
		Nevadan orogeny: { Infiltration of mineral-bearing quartz veins into fractured rocks
		Metamorphism of older rocks on contact with granitic rocks
		Intrusion of granitic batholith
		Folding, crushing and faulting
		Uprise of sediments from inland sea basin }
		Intrusions of serpentine rocks
		Interbedding of basalt with sediments
		Marine deposition
		Volcanism
		Marine deposition
			Age
			
			Quartz veins
			Granodiorite and related rocks
			Dike rocks
			Serpentine
			Mariposa slate
			Amador volcanic group
			  Agua Fria formation
			  Logtown Ridge and Penon Blanco formation
			  Cosumnes and Hunter Valley formations
				Age
				
				40
				
				155

	Triassic	Marine deposition, including coral reefs Volcanism	Sailor Canyon formation Brock shale **Hosselkus limestone** Volcanic rocks	35 190
Paleozoic		Folding and unconformity		
	Carboniferous and Permian	Marine deposition, including coral reefs Extensive sedimentation throughout Sierra Nevada province	*Calaveras formation including limestones:* { Clipper Gap formation Delhi formation Cape Horn slate Relief quartzite Kanaka conglomerate formation Tightner volcanic formation Blue Canyon marine formation }	300
	Devonian	Marine deposition	Taylorsville formation	
	Silurian	Marine deposition, including coral reefs	Montgomery limestone Grizzly formation	
	Ordovician Cambrian	Not known in Sierra Nevada		500
Pre-Cambrian		Not known in Sierra Nevada		Indefinite 1300 2 billion (age of earth)

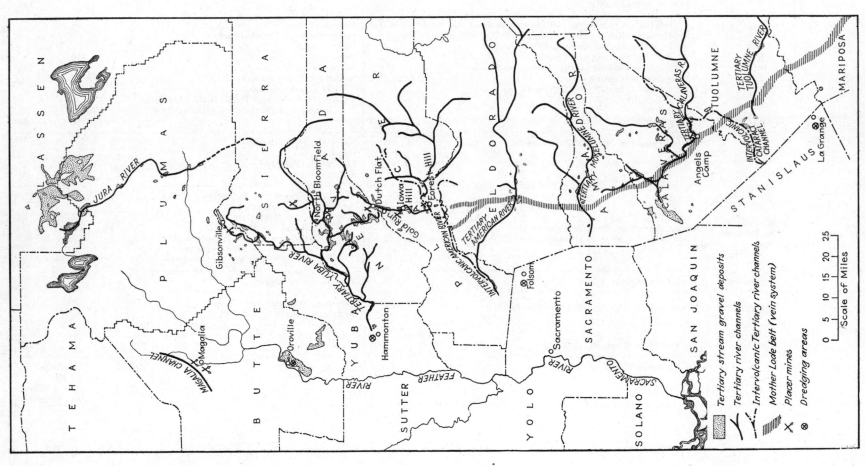

Fig. 1. Map showing the main courses of the Tertiary River channels as mapped by Lindgren and other members of the U. S. Geological Survey. The positions of the Mother Lode and various Tertiary gravel deposits are also shown, together with the location of some of the principal placer mines. *Prepared from map by Olaf P. Jenkins, State Division of Mines; cut by courtesy of Engineering and Mining Journal, Nov. 1934.*

batholithic granites—form what is commonly known as the "Bedrock series" of the Sierra Nevada and all of the gold-bearing quartz veins are enclosed in these hard rocks of the early geologic periods.

The only definite rock record of Cretaceous (which followed the Jurassic) in the Sierra Nevada is a series of sandstones and shales (not metamorphosed) of Upper Cretaceous age that lie well down on the western flanks and on the deeply eroded surface of the Bedrock series. This means that there is a break in geologic evidence representing the unrecorded time of the early Cretaceous period; a break caused by a long erosion period. Even the tops of the quartz veins were reached. The rocks of this early mountainous surface were torn down and rolled into boulders and sands and deposited in a Cretaceous sea that spread out and filled a basin where the Great Valley and Coast Ranges now are located. The mountain range of the ancestral Sierra even extended as far as the center of the present Great Valley during early Cretaceous, but erosional removal of the mountains' western front had the surface effect of moving the range eastward.

This brings the geologic history to another most interesting epoch of events which have had a profound effect upon the entire civilization of California.

The erosion period of the Cretaceous laid bare the upper, richer parts of the gold-bearing quartz veins, and the episode which followed resulted in releasing, removing, depositing and concentrating the gold from the upper portions of the veins into placer deposits of unbelievable richness. The gold-releasing episode was a period of geologic quiet, not mountain-making nor destructive erosion. It occurred during the Eocene period and particularly during its beginning or Paleocene time when the climate was semi-tropical and humid. The effect of this environment on a land surface which had already been eroded partly to base level and partly to rolling hills, bordering a lagoon-margined sea, was to cause deep decay and weathering resulting in the formation of deep red lateritic soil such as one finds in the tropics. The rocks were so badly decayed that clay was formed and floated into the lagoons where it was deposited along with decayed vegetation to form lignite. Quartz particles did not decay with the feldspar but remained as quartz fragments, pebbles, and quartz sand. In places they were cemented together by iron oxide, weathered from the rock. The gold in the veins was thus separated from its matrix and released. It then found its way, because of its high specific gravity, to the lower parts of crevices and into the beds of swift streams, where it was caught in the natural rock-riffles of slate and schist. These Eocene streams, however, were streams of 50 million years ago and they were destined to undergo entrapment and to be preserved until a much later time.

The entrapment of streams, or rather of the boulders, gravels, and sand deposited in their channels and along their banks, was effected in the following manner: A fall of finely divided, light-colored, volcanic ash

(rhyolitic in composition) initiated a period of volcanism as the epoch of Eocene time closed. This period of volcanism continued in Oligocene and Miocene time. The volcanic ash was washed into the streams where it dammed them, formed lakes, covered them, and diverted the drainage. The volcanism did not wane, but increased in vigor. It was accompanied by earth movements and severe earthquakes. The low hills of the area started to rise with the result that the flow of the newly diverted streams was accelerated. Darker colored lavas (andesite), mud flows, volcanic tuff and ash spread far and wide, filling all depressions, and finally leaving only the higher mountains and peaks standing as islands above this steaming sea of volcanic mud.

This extreme activity of volcanism was extended far to the north, even to the Columbia lava plateau of eastern Oregon and Washington, and there were outbursts in many other parts of California and the West in general. All these events took place largely in the Miocene and Pliocene epochs of the Tertiary.

Finally toward the close of the Pliocene, as this period of volcanism came to an end, a new epoch of disturbance came into being. Volcanoes broke out at the Dardanelles and elsewhere high on the Sierra, and one molten flow of basic lava followed the canyon of a stream cut largely in ash as far as Knights Ferry. Later erosion of the softer ash left the hard black lava stream, sinuous as a river in form, high and dry as we see Tuolumne Table Mountain today.

Earthquakes must have been of tremendous intensity, resulting from great earth movements and faulting which prevailed during late Pliocene and early Pleistocene. The Sierra Nevada province moved largely as a unit, tilting westward and breaking along the eastern escarpment. Accumulated fault displacements on this eastern front amounted to many thousands of feet. The streams were accelerated manyfold, and torrents swept down the western slope of the Sierra, cutting deep and rugged canyons. The high Sierras became enveloped and packed in snow; then glaciers crept down from cirques, their places of origin near the highest peaks.

In many places, especially in the lower slopes of the Sierra Nevada where the foothills begin to merge into the Great Valley, the volcanic cover of soft ash has been largely stripped by erosion from the harder surface of bedrock. Thus were exhumed parts of the old Eocene surface, which was formed 50 million years ago, with its weathered mantle and deep red soil, its cover of white quartz gravel, and its rich concentrations of gold lying in the beds of thousands of ancient stream channels.

This old rolling surface now remains between the newly formed canyons. To the east it rises gradually in elevation while the canyons increase in depth. It is easily understandable why these Eocene channels, originally controlled in direction by bedrock structure over which the water flowed, have no parallelism to the new streams born on the westward sloping surface of the widespread volcanic cover, and destined later to cut deeply into a rising surface and to become entrenched even to the granite core of the mountain range. Though born on the volcanic cover, the present streams have thus cut much deeper into the bedrock than did the ancient channels. The new streams often cut and robbed fragments of the older Eocene channels and washed their gravels and their gold into the recent river beds.

This the forty-niners soon found out and followed the gold to its source, often by drift mining under the volcanic cover where it had not yet been removed by erosion. They found that the richest placers were those of white quartz gravels not intermixed with the softer volcanic ash. They found that the richer ancient channels generally followed the trend of the geologic structure of the bedrock, which once guided their course,

while the later streams in the volcanic ash lay athwart the direction of the buried hills and valleys. They found that the rhyolite ash or "pipe-clay," generally lay directly upon the earliest quartz gravels and in places these gravels and their gold had been robbed by intervolcanic water courses which were also buried along with the Eocene gravels.

The complexity of the structure of all these inter-related gravel channels is extreme, and for that reason the distribution of the gold within them is variable. The whole story is closely interwoven with the earlier history of the bedrock, the position of gold-bearing veins in the bedrock, and their removal and redeposition by erosion. We are still far from having solved the complete history of these intricate events which resulted in the unique and interesting features of the Sierran Gold Belt.

FIG. 2.   Partly cemented ancient gravel channel deposits exposed by hydrau- licking in the Omega mine. Below the gravel is the bedrock schist and at the contact is the concentration of placer gold. Above the gravels are finer-grained deposits of sand and clay which have been partly washed away.

FIG. 3.   Clay pit in the Ione formation (Eocene) south of the town of Ione, Amador County.

FIG. 4.   View northwest across the covered bridge at O'Byrne Ferry on the road to Copperopolis. Tuolumne Table Mountain has been eroded through by the Stanislaus River.

FIG. 6.   The very rough lava surface of the top of Tuolumne Table Mountain as seen west of Jamestown.

FIG. 5.   Old railroad cut through Table Mountain northwest of Jamestown. Latite lava columns are exposed on the left. To the right is the schist rim of the old channel which the lava occupies. The railroad has been dismantled since the picture was taken.

FIG. 7.   Detail of lava columns exposed in railroad cut through Table Mountain northwest of Jamestown.

FIG. 8.   Syncline in Logtown volcanics on South Fork of the Calaveras River one mile south of Ione.

FIG. 10.   Sharply folded anticline in Mariposa slate on Ganns Creek, Mariposa County.

FIG. 9.   Outcrop of "tombstone rocks" in the schistose bedrock near Campo Seco.

FIG. 11.   Stream-worn quartz boulders of ancient gold-bearing channel near the Sixteen-to-One mine at Alleghany, Sierra County. *Photo by Wm. O. Jenkins*.

HISTORY OF MINING AND MILLING METHODS IN CALIFORNIA
By C. A. Logan

PLACER MINING

Simple Early Day Mining Methods

The action of water had been chiefly responsible for the formation of the rich placer deposits of gold sought by the pioneers, and it was the principal agent used by them in winning the gold. The richness of the most accessible deposits found by the earliest miners along the stream courses permitted them to make a profit from working small quantities of auriferous gravel in the miner's pan, batea or horn. Soon it was found that the miner's cradle or rocker would permit a man to work many times as much gravel in a day as with a pan, so that he could make a good profit from poorer gravel. As the number of miners increased, the richer diggings were exhausted and it became necessary to work more gravel for a given amount of gold. The long tom was next introduced by men from Georgia. This was a trough of boards 12 feet long, 8 inches deep, 12 to 15 inches wide at the head and widening to 2 or 2½ feet at the lower end, which terminated in a sheet of iron with upturned edges. This iron was punched with small holes that permitted the gold and finer sand to fall into a box below while the coarsest rock could be cast aside. The long tom required a steady stream of water. For this purpose the first mining ditch in California is claimed to have been dug at Coyote Hill, Nevada City, in March, 1850, to supply miners' long toms. It was about two miles long. The first miner's sluice box is also said to have been originated in Nevada County. It was a V-flume of two boards, a type which later came into wide use for transporting lumber. The miners soon changed to a sluice box made of three boards, which at first had a bottom board 12 inches wide with sides 10 inches high. A number of these boxes, fitted end to end, made a string of sluices of greater capacity than the long tom. Later, as developed for use in river mining, flumes 18 to 40 feet wide, with sides 6 feet high, were used to carry the entire low-water flow of one or more branches of the American, Yuba and other rivers in the gold belt, so that the beds of these streams could be worked.

As the placer miners thus exhausted the gravel that could be profitably worked by their methods on the banks, bars, and even from the beds of the rivers, they began to follow "prospects" higher in the hills among the tributary streams. There they noticed deposits of gravel on the canyon sides and on benches of land sometimes hundreds of feet above the present rivers. These were ancient buried river channels. The gravel was similar in appearance to that of the modern rivers and some experimental work proved it also carried gold. It was not long after these hillside deposits were found that some miner, whose name is not known, conceived the idea for a new and cheaper way to work them. By this method, which came to be called ground sluicing, a stream of water was brought to the top of a bank of gravel and allowed to flow down over the face. It softened the gravel and with a little help from the miner, carried it along to a natural sluice prepared on the bedrock below. A man was thus able to handle in a day with very little shoveling much more than he had previously been able to lift into his sluice box or long tom. By a later adaptation of this method, the gravel in the bed of a stream with sufficient grade could be worked by damming the stream and releasing the flow of water at regular intervals by means of an automatic gate. The large volume of water released carried gravel and boulders down stream until the volume of material to be shoveled into sluices for the final cleanup was reduced to a minimum. This was called "booming" or "hushing." Other variations of ground sluicing were practiced.

Hydraulic Mining

Edward E. Mattison, working at American Hill, just north of Nevada City in 1853, is credited with first making use of water under pressure to undermine and wash gravel into sluice boxes. In this pioneer plant for hydraulic mining, water was brought in a ditch to a point on the hillside 40 to 60 feet above a bank of gravel and thence taken from a penstock or intake reservoir through canvas hose four or five inches in diameter to a point in front of the gravel. There the water was directed through a sheet iron nozzle against the base of the gravel bank, undermining it and causing it to fall, whence it could be easily washed into sluice boxes laid in a trench cut in the bedrock to receive it. Only 25 to 50 miners' inches of water was used in this project. The method was introduced at Yankee Jims, Placer County, in 1853 by Colonel William McClure, who had visited Mattison's mine that year. Canvas hose was soon in great demand, and a number of inventors began to make "gadgets" for use in this new process, which Mattison made no effort to patent. Thus began the great system of reservoirs and canals needed to supply water for dozens of large mining ventures in all the counties from Plumas southward to Tuolumne. Hydraulic mining flourished in the region for about 25 years until 1880. In 1867, there were 5328 miles of main canals, with probably 800 miles more of branch ditches built at a cost of $15,575,400. Some of the water systems extended into the higher portions of the Sierra Nevada. Main ditches were usually 8 to 15 feet wide at the top, 4 to 6 feet wide at the bottom and three feet or more in depth. Water was carried across valleys and around rocky points first in wooden flumes, which were later largely replaced by heavy iron pipes from 20 to 40 inches in diameter. These systems were often owned by companies that sold the water to miners. In later years, after hydraulic mining was enjoined, many of the canals and reservoirs became part of the Pacific Gas & Electric Company's hydroelectric system, and the Nevada Irrigation District's system draws water from reservoirs and ditches of one of these systems which once supplied immense hydraulic mines.

As hydraulic mining began to be applied to larger deposits the equipment used and the method of operation underwent rapid change, all in the direction of greater working capacity and lower unit cost.

Canvas hose was soon replaced by iron pipe. Special heavy iron or steel spouts and nozzles, such as the Monitor, Giant or Dictator were invented and put in use. Their modern versions have double joints to give horizontal and vertical movement, and deflectors to utilize the reactive force of the water to permit easy turning. The largest sizes, under a head of 400 feet will handle a flow of over 4500 cubic feet of water a minute. In ordinary practice, however, in California, in 1867, a flow of 500 miner's inches (about 750 cubic feet per minute) was considered a satisfactory amount. This was increased with the opening of large mines with banks several hundred feet high, and the use of 1000 to 1500 miner's inches of water per giant became common, with heads as high as 450 feet. The water was often assisted by "bank blasting", where T-shaped adits were run into the gravel bank, or a shaft with short drifts at the bottom was sunk, the arms of the T being loaded with several thousand pounds of black powder or low-strength dynamite which was fired to break down the bank. Long tunnels also had to be run in many cases to give drainage through the rim of the old channel. In spite of these heavy expenses, hydraulic mining was cheap, and permitted working large bodies of gravel at a profit even when their gold content was 10 cents a cubic yard or less.

Fig. 1.   A view of the Mother Lode in Amador County showing the Bunker Hill mine in foreground, the Treasure mine in the center, and the headframe of Fremont mine in the left background.

Drift Mining

Although the mining of buried ancient river channels by means of shafts and adits was started very soon after the outcrops of gravel were noticed on the hillsides, and at about the same time as hydraulic mining, it has not suffered from the restrictions laid upon hydraulicking. The hundreds of miles of such channels, the oldest of which were flowing streams as early as Cretaceous time on what is now the western slope of the Sierra Nevada, were buried and preserved under volcanic mud and coarser rock ejected by eruptions in the higher Sierra Nevada. The ideal method of mining these channels is to determine if possible the lowest available point in the trough of the channel and to open it by running an adit from an outlet or through one rim to give drainage and permit following the channel upstream, with the adit either on the bedrock or in bedrock far enough below the gravel to give a solid roof, through which raises are put up and working faces opened across the payable width of gravel. Some channels have been followed and mined for several miles. The Forest Hill Divide in Placer County was the most celebrated of the drift mining districts. The mining method resembles that used in coal mining. Much of the gravel was found to be cemented and had to be milled or washed several times after lying in the open air to aid disintegration. Stamp mills with coarse screens were found to be most suitable for milling cemented gravel.

Dredging

The pioneers made a number of abortive attempts to dredge gold from the river beds. In 1897, gold dredging with a single-lift elevator type of bucket dredge was attempted on Yuba River, but the first successful operation was started in March 1898 at Oroville by W. P. Hammon and Thomas Couch. This dredge had open-link buckets of three cubic feet capacity and a tailing stacker. Close-connected buckets, belt conveyor stackers for tailing, and electric power were introduced in 1901. On the American River near Folsom, dredging was started early in 1899 by Colorado Pacific Gold Dredging Company. These earliest dredges used steam for power and worked 30,000 to 35,000 cubic yards of gravel a month. The American genius for large scale operation can be seen in the steady increase in yardage and depth capacity. W. P. Hammon and R. D. Evans started in the Yuba River field in 1903 with a dredge having buckets of six cubic feet capacity and a shaking screen. It could dig 60 feet below water level. Revolving screens appear to have become standard in 1905. Since then, this type of dredge has been put on practically every gold-bearing river in northern California, but the most important fields have been Yuba River near Hammonton, American River near Folsom, and Feather River near Oroville. Gold production of over $100,000,000 from Yuba County, over $95,000,000 from Sacramento County and about $60,000,000 from Butte County since dredging started has been made principally by bucket dredges. They have been increased in size and capacity until the largest, now operating in the Yuba River field, all have 18-cubic foot buckets and dig more than 100 feet below the level of the ponds on which they float. The weekly capacity of a large modern dredge may reach 125,000 cubic yards. The largest and latest, Yuba No. 20, weighs 3700 tons, has a total length of 540 feet; carries 135 buckets of 18 cubic feet capacity each, and digs 124 feet below water level. Most of the gold recovered in dredging is saved on Hungarian type riffles arranged in rows crosswise of the dredge. These receive the fine material, under $\frac{1}{2}$ inch, which passes through the perforations in the large trommel or screen into which the digging buckets dump the gravel. The average gold content of gravel (10¢ to 15¢ a cubic yard) handled by dredgers and the cost of operation (5¢ to 10¢ a cubic yard) are quite close to those realized years ago in hydraulic mining. But because of the small crew (three or four men per shift) required to handle a large yardage, the dredge operator is nearly independent of the cost of labor, which now hampers other forms of gold mining.

The dragline dredge, which generally is operated to supply gravel to a barge carrying a gravel washing plant, was widely used in California in the decade prior to the last war to work shallow gravel deposits too small to justify a bucket dredge. About 200 such outfits, each employing about 10 men and digging about 2000 to 2500 cubic yards of gravel a day, were in operation on small streams in this state in 1940-41. Their operating cost is about double that of a bucket dredge and they are limited usually to gravel not over 20 feet deep. The dragline is of the type in wide use by earth-moving contractors, using Diesel power and having a bucket preferably of two cubic yards capacity or more. The washing plant, floating on a pond dug by the dragline, is a lighter, cheaper and simpler version of those used on bucket dredges.

QUARTZ MINING

First Gold-Quartz Discoveries

The Mariposa mine, at the south side of the town of Mariposa, was discovered in the spring of 1849 by Kit Carson, the famous scout, and two associates. In July 1849, a stamp mill, probably the first in the State, was crushing ore from this mine. The outcrop of the vein yielded rich specimen ore, and the first mining was nothing more than the digging of shallow holes to remove this ore, which was broken by hand before crushing in the mill. The latter had no means of amalgamating the gold, which had to be saved by washing the pulp in a rocker. Soon after, an arrastre was built to handle the stamp mill pulp.

Gold-bearing quartz was found on Gold Hill at Grass Valley in June 1850 and was so rich and plentiful for a time that the miners feared gold would lose its value. The first gold quartz claims, limited to 60 feet by 120 feet, were located on the Mother Lode in Amador County in 1850,

and probably during the same year in the other mining counties. At the time there were many Mexican placer miners in the region from El Dorado County southward, and they introduced the arrastre for crushing the ore and amalgamating the gold. Soon there were hundreds of these slow but efficient machines in operation, notably at Nashville, El Dorado County and Carson Hill, Calaveras County, crushing selected ore taken from the surface or shallow holes that required only hand tools.

The Stamp Mill Replaces the Arrastre

The arrastre was too slow for the Americans. The stamp mill, previously used in Europe, had been introduced into the southern Appalachian gold mines years before the California discovery, and men who had seen it there before coming west are credited with designing the first crude mills of the kind. These mills had square wooden stems and square iron shoes. There was no provision for rotation, a point which the travellers had forgotten, as rotation had been provided in the Appalachian mill. Ore had to be broken by hand and shoveled into the mill.

Early Struggles of the Quartz Miners

The quartz mining industry had many ups and downs in the first 15 years after these early discoveries. In a private report made in 1864, Professor William Ashburner stated that "in 1858 there were upwards of 280 quartz mills in California, each one of which was supplied with quartz from one or more veins. The number of stamps in these mills was 2610 and the total cost of the whole mill property of this nature in the state exceeded $3,000,000. In the summer of 1861 . . . I made a careful and thorough examination of all the quartz mills and mines of the state, and could only find between 40 and 50 in successful operation, several of which were at that time leading a very precarious existence." The discovery of the Comstock Lode in Nevada in 1859 had attracted great numbers of California miners. Actual progress in sinking on the veins was slow. The Hayward, now the Old Eureka mine, being worked by Central Eureka Mining Company at Sutter Creek, had reached an inclined depth of 1230 feet, and was the deepest mine in the state in 1867, having been in continuous operation since 1852. The Eureka mine, now part of the Idaho-Maryland at Grass Valley, was only 100 feet deep in 1863. The North Star mine shaft at Grass Valley, probably the deepest in that district at that time, had reached an inclined depth of 750 feet in 1867, and the vein had been explored underground for a length of 1000 feet. At last, quartz mining was becoming firmly established.

Innovations and Improvements

The early-day shafts were sunk as inclines following the veins on the dip. Steam engines were used mostly for power. Hand drills and black powder were used entirely until 1868, when the first air drills and dynamite were introduced, although the widespread use of air drills for stoping ore did not come for 30 years. These last two innovations did much to increase the speed of underground development, resulting in lower gold content per ton, and called for more mill capacity. The gravity stamp was gradually increased in weight from 250 pounds to 1250 or 1500 pounds each. Self-feeders, actuated by one stamp in each battery of five, were provided. Before 1870, the foundries of San Francisco, particularly the Union Iron Works, had become recognized as makers of stamp mills and it was in this state that these mills were brought to the high standards that made them the principal means for reducing gold ore for 50 years. Square wooden stems were supplanted in the middle sixties by cylindrical stamp stems of iron fitted with tappets which, when engaged with cams on the horizontal power shaft, lifted and rotated the stamp. Outside amalgamation was provided by long plates of copper, which were first silver plated, then coated with a thin layer of liquid mercury. Rock breakers, such as the Blake crusher, were introduced in California in 1861 to prepare ore for the stamps. The self-feeder, the rock breaker, heavier stamps and increased running speed gave the stamps greatly increased capacity.

Treatment of Concentrate

The concentration of the sulphide, which makes up 1 percent to 2 percent of most of our gold ores and nearly always carries enough gold to be worth saving, was first made in sluices with riffles, similar to those of the placer miner. In the sixties, Cornish buddles and other European devices were used, and new types of concentrators were invented. In July 1867, George Johnston and E. G. Smith patented an endless belt vanner of rubber, set on a slight incline between rollers 8 or 12 feet apart. It was driven slowly toward the upper roller and also had a short, rapid motion sideways. It proved so effective in saving concentrate that it and the similar Frue vanner, perfected in 1878, became standard equipment where stamp mills were used. The chlorination process, previously known in Europe as the Plattner process, for recovering gold from concentrate, was brought to California and improved to the point where it was widely used until cyanidation was introduced in 1896.

It will be seen from these side lights that California quartz mining and milling practice drew freely from European methods, which were usually improved and modernized here. The mining engineers and metallurgists of this state became so well known for their work that their advice and services were sought when new districts were opened in foreign countries.

Development of Water Power

For a long time after quartz mining started, steam engines using wood fuel obtained locally were the principal source of power for mines and mills. The development of large water systems for hydraulic mining, and the increasing cost and scarcity of wood for fuel, led to the use of water power, under high pressure, to operate tangential or impulse wheels. By the middle eighties, nearly all of the principal quartz mines were using Knight, Pelton or Donnelly wheels of the impulse type to supply their power needs. Of the three makes, the Pelton wheel has been most successful, and the Pelton Water Wheel Company is still a going concern in San Francisco, their product being used in later years for generating hydroelectric power. This Pelton wheel is highly efficient, and made possible the introduction of electric power in the mining regions of the West before public utilities had entered the field.

Development and Use of Hydroelectric Power

The first recorded use of electric power for the operation of mining or quartz milling machinery in California was at the Dalmatia mine in El Dorado County in February 1890. Water under $112\frac{1}{2}$ feet pressure was delivered to a Pelton wheel 7 feet in diameter, which operated an electric generator of 126 horsepower, and current was transmitted over a line about one mile long to the plant. Pacific Gas and Electric Company has acknowledged its debt to the California miners and the tangential water wheel. It is not too much to say that the company owed its origin to the hydraulic miners and the Pelton wheel.

BIBLIOGRAPHY

ANONYMOUS, California's debt to the miner: Pacific Gas and Electric Progress, vol. 1, no. 8, p. 2, 1924.

BROWNE, J. ROSS, Mineral resources of the states and territories west of the Rocky Mountains for 1867: U. S. Treasury Dept., 367 pp., Washington, D. C., 1868.

DE GROOT, HENRY, El Dorado County: California Min. Bur. Rept. 10, pp. 169-182, 1890.

LOGAN, C. A., Mother Lode gold belt of California: California Div. Mines Bull. 108, 240 pp., 1934.

JOHNSTON, GEORGE, Brief history of concentration and description of the Johnston concentrator: In California mines and minerals, pp. 439-441, California Miners Association, San Francisco, 1899.

GEOLOGIC MAPS AND NOTES ALONG HIGHWAY 49

By OLIVER E. BOWEN JR. and RICHARD A. CRIPPEN JR.

OUTLINE OF REPORT

Introduction

California State Highway 49, variously known as the Mother Lode Highway or the Golden Highway, traverses 277 miles of the Sierra Nevada, beginning at Mariposa on the south and ending at Sattley on the north. It passes through nine counties, each of which represents an important part of the Sierran Gold Belt.

This entire region has come to be known generally as the Mother Lode Country, but more technically speaking, the Mother Lode is a belt of gold-bearing quartz veins which appears to start at Mariposa and to terminate at Georgetown in El Dorado County. It forms a more or less continuous belt of quartz veins that occupy a fault zone approximately one mile wide and 120 airline miles long. The 10-mile segment of this belt between Jackson and Plymouth is its richest section and was the source of one-half the gold produced in the entire 120-mile extent, which has amounted to a quarter of a billion dollars. It is noteworthy that this 10-mile segment lies at the bend in the belt where its trend changes from northwest to nearly due north. The fault structure with which the Mother Lode quartz veins are associated may possibly extend 50 miles farther northward to Downieville, but Highway 49 leaves the Mother Lode at Placerville and swings 10 or 15 miles to the west, traversing the even more productive Grass Valley-Nevada City district and other gold-bearing areas of the northern Sierra Nevada.

The veins range from great white quartz masses 150 feet wide, down to stringers less than the thickness of one's little finger. The thickness of a vein is no criterion as to its potential value. Rich pocket mines such as those of Jackass Hill were found largely in narrow veinlets, whereas the massive silica-carbonate rock of the Peñon Blanco is practically barren of gold.

Mining methods and techniques developed in the California gold belt have spread to the far corners of the earth and have become standard practice everywhere. Many famous technicians and financiers had their training in the Mother Lode Country before attaining even greater distinction and achievement in other fields. Bret Harte and Mark Twain owe much of their reputation to the gold country, and through their stories the romance of the region has become familiar to all the world.

Although so much has been written of the history, romance, and folklore of the Sierran Gold Belt, little of general geologic interest has been published for the use of the traveler. The following notes on geology along Highway 49 attempt to correlate the geologic, mining, historic, scenic, and cultural features encountered as one travels north along the route from Mariposa to Yuba Pass and Sierra Valley.

The geologic maps, which these notes accompany, form a continuous strip through the Sierran Gold Belt, and cover an area a few miles wide on either side of Highway 49. In the preparation of the maps and the descriptions, material was assembled from various sources of information, published and unpublished, supplemented by field notes. To facilitate the reading of these notes while traveling, footnote references have been omitted, but sources of information are acknowledged in the preface to this volume.

MARIPOSA TO COULTERVILLE—MAP 1

The junction of Highways 140 and 49, one-half mile north of the town of Mariposa, marks the southern terminus of Highway 49. Mariposa, the county seat of Mariposa County, is on the tourist route to Yosemite Valley, and its fine old County Courthouse, a white frame structure erected in 1854, has been in use continuously since that date. The town lies at an elevation slightly above 2000 feet in a northwesterly trending valley bordered to east and west by ridges of moderate height. Vegetation in this region is sparse and is composed largely of digger pines, small oak trees, and patches of chaparral. There are a few small stands of yellow pine on protected north slopes southwest of Mariposa. Early day logging operations removed much of the timber in this region.

A mile south of Mariposa, in the vicinity of the County Fair Grounds, are the dumps and partly caved workings of the Mariposa mine, which was discovered in 1849 by Kit Carson and two associates. As early as July 1849, Palmer, Cook, and Company were running a stamp mill on ore from the Mariposa mine. In 1859 John C. Frémont wrested the title to the mine from its original owners when accorded title to the Las Mariposas grant of 44,000 acres. Mines of the Las Mariposas grant also included the Pine Tree, Josephine, Princeton, and many minor workings such as the Peñon Blanco claim. The latter is one of the longest claims on record, title having been recorded before length limitations on mining claims became law. The Mariposa mine had its heyday between 1900 and 1915, 1901 being the peak year. Estimated total production for the mine is $2,193,205. Workings reached a depth of about 1550 feet along a 60° to 70° incline or about 1350 feet vertically. The veins lie in meta-augite andesite of the Peñon Blanco formation, locally called greenstone.

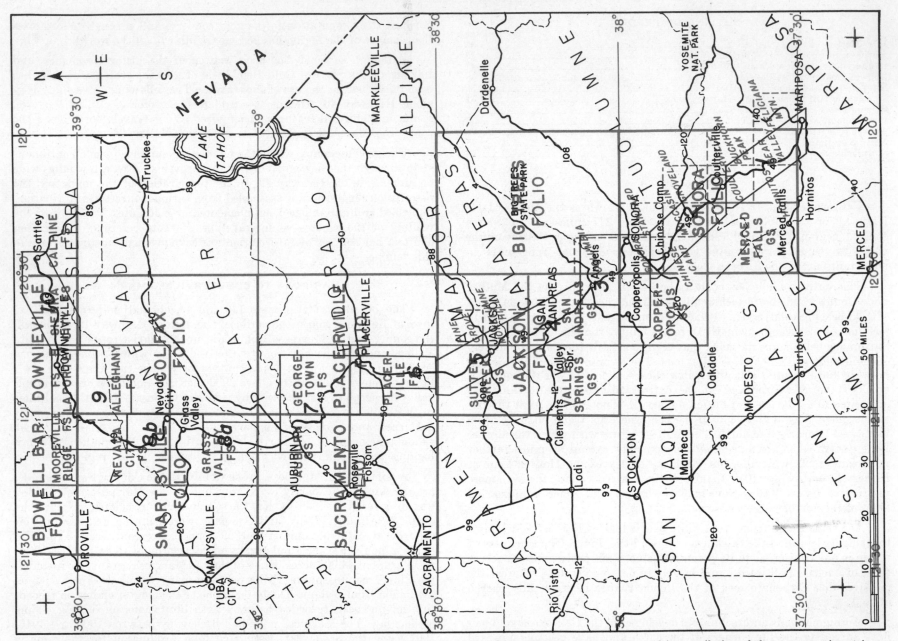

FIG. 1. Map of the northern Sierra Nevada showing the highways, in black; the topographic quadrangles which were used in compilation of the accompanying strip maps, in brown; the position of each strip map section in relation to these quadrangles, in red; and, as shown in the map index, the sources of geologic data used in making the strip maps.

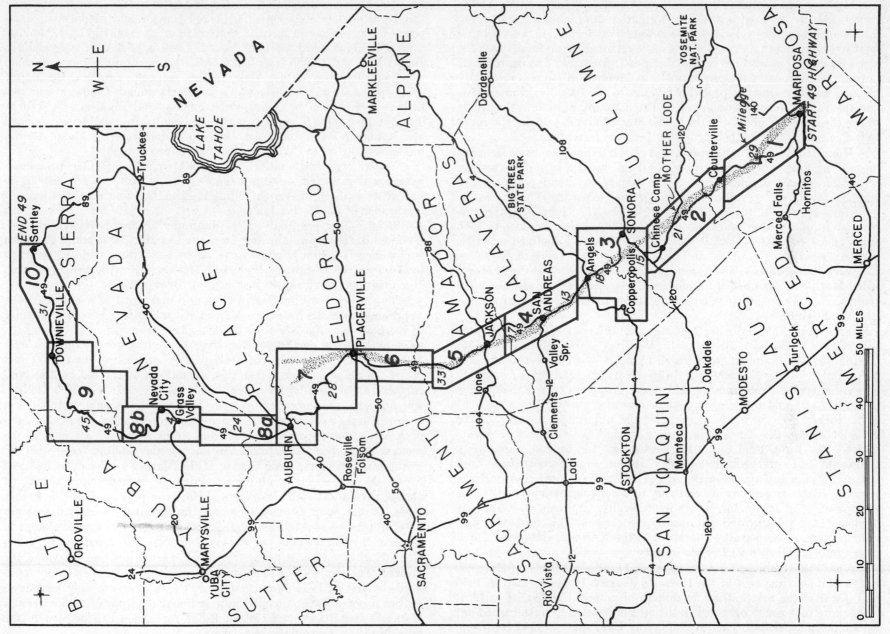

FIG. 2. Map of the northern Sierra Nevada showing the highways, principally Highway 49, and the mileages between towns. The position of the strip maps in relation to Highway 49 and the Mother Lode, and the approximate position of the Mother Lode zone (shaded) are also shown.

Highway 49 begins in meta-volcanic* rocks of Jurassic age of the Peñon Blanco or Logtown Ridge formation and passes successively through meta-sedimentary rocks of the Calaveras formation, a serpentine intrusive body, more meta-sediments of doubtful age, and finally into the black slates and sandstones of the Mariposa formation. The narrow belt of rocks to the west of the serpentine near Mount Bullion was originally mapped as Calaveras but probably belongs to the Amador group and is Jurassic rather than Paleozoic in age. From Mount Bullion to the divide where the highway begins its drop into Merced River canyon, the rocks on both sides of the road belong to the Mariposa formation.

Mount Bullion, 4.7 miles northwest of Mariposa, was once a flourishing mining center being the site of the Princeton mine and the supply center for placer diggings close by. Evidences of hand placering are manifest along every stream bed and gravel exposure. The Princeton mine was opened in 1852 and up to 1933 was the largest producer in Mariposa County. Gold in excess of $4,228,000 was recovered up to 1915 since when very little work has been done. The shaft is inclined at angles varying between 45° and 60° and falls to an inclined depth of 1660 feet. The vertical depth is slightly greater than 1350 feet. The Carlo Marre store, Mariposa Chamber of Commerce Historical Marker, and the more recent Frank Trabucco store, across the street, mark the center of present day Mount Bullion.

Four-tenths of a mile north of Mount Bullion a road from Hornitos and Merced Falls joins Highway 49. Hornitos is the hub of a very old mining district, the town having been founded by Spanish Californians before gold rush days. The Mount Bullion-Hornitos road cuts successively across the strike of Mariposa and Amador group rocks and then enters exposures of Guadeloupe granodiorite near the town of Hornitos. The Ruth Pierce mine is at the contact of the uppermost member of the Amador group, the Agua Fria formation, and the Guadeloupe granodiorite. The Agua Fria formation consists of thin-bedded, hard, platy sediments and interbedded volcanics. It lies, in different areas, both unconformably and gradationally on the Peñon Blanco or Logtown Ridge member of the Amador group and may be a nonvolcanic member of that formation. The latter formation is, typically, a green meta-andesite agglomerate having prominent augite phenocrysts. This formation persists in more or less parallel alignment to the Mariposa slate from Mariposa County well into El Dorado County.

The Washington or Jenny Lind mine, 1½ miles northeast of Hornitos has been one of the best in the Hornitos district. It was located in 1850 and installed the first milling machinery of note in the district in 1851. The stamp mill which operated in the 50's is reputed to have turned out $1,000 in gold per day. The vertical Jenny Lind shaft is 1540 feet deep. The recorded production is $1,099,000 and the estimated production, $2,247,000.

The Mount Gaines mine, located five miles northeast of Hornitos on the Hornitos-Bear Valley road, is the only major gold producer in Mariposa County. It has an inclined shaft with an average dip of 30° having a total inclined depth of 1322 feet. The ore is of sulfide type and the veins dip at 30° to 35° from horizontal. Steeply dipping veins are more common along the Mother Lode, in this respect, therefore, the Mount Gaines veins are unusual. The wall rock is meta-andesite and vein minerals include pyrite, quartz, chalcopyrite, galena, and sphalerite as well as disseminated gold. Bornite, proustite, arsenopyrite, and argentite have been found in small quantities. Early production of the Mount Gaines totaled $1,250,000 to 1911. No recent figures are available.

Two and two-tenths miles south of the town of Bear Valley, prominent outcrops of quartz can be seen to the west of the highway. These stand up like white walls on the gently rolling land surface and mark the trace of one branch of the Mother Lode.

Bear Valley, originally called Simpsonville, was promoted by J. C. Frémont during his administration of the Las Mariposas grant. The town is now largely a ruin of small stone, adobe, and frame buildings marked by Division of Highways Historical Marker 331. Another road from Hornitos joins Highway 49 just north of Bear Valley.

Two miles north of Bear Valley and one-tenth of a mile past the divide marking the drop into Merced River canyon, a broad shoulder in the highway affords a good parking place from which to observe the panorama to the northwest. The river has cut a gorge which is over 1200 feet below the level of Bear Valley and more than 2000 feet below the ridge tops on either side. Remnants of the old rolling land surface can be seen on the ridge to the east of the river. Hell Hollow, which is a narrow gorge tributary to the Merced, lies immediately below the road to the northwest. The first fossils by which the age of the Mariposa slates were determined came from outcrops in Hell Hollow. To the east of the Merced River and more or less paralleling its course, the white outcrops of the main branch of the Mother Lode can be followed for miles. In the vicinity of Whites Gulch, the quartz outcrops take an abrupt turn and strike almost due north. It is possible that the Mother Lode, at that point, is offset by a cross fault, but work on that area has been insufficient to establish the fact conclusively. The abrupt change in strike of the Mother Lode outcrops is very noticeable from several points along Highway 49 as it drops from Bear Valley into the canyon of the Merced. The Mother Lode thrust fault system has displaced many thousands of feet of beds. More than 15,000 feet of strata may have been cut out in some places. Steeply dipping linear outcrops of meta-volcanics of the Peñon Blanco or Logtown Ridge formation can be seen in the hillside to the west of the Merced River.

The mine buildings, cyanide tanks, and adits of the Pine Tree and Josephine mines lie in a gulch between the two major switchbacks between Bear Valley and the Merced River bridge. These mines were

---
*The prefix *meta* means *metamorphosed*, implying that the rocks so designated have undergone profound change due to heat and pressure.

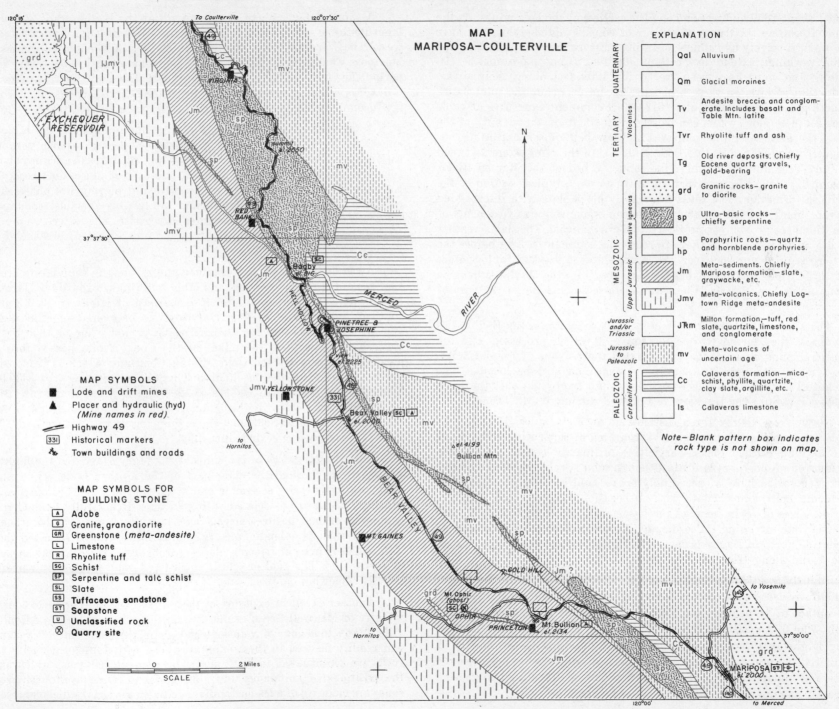

MAP I
MARIPOSA-COULTERVILLE

EXPLANATION

QUATERNARY
Qal Alluvium
Qm Glacial moraines

TERTIARY
Volcanics
Tv Andesite breccia and conglomerate. Includes basalt and Table Mtn. latite
Tvr Rhyolite tuff and ash
Tg Old river deposits. Chiefly Eocene quartz gravels, gold-bearing

MESOZOIC
Intrusive igneous
grd Granitic rocks—granite to diorite
sp Ultra-basic rocks—chiefly serpentine
qp Porphyritic rocks—quartz and hornblende porphyries.
hp
Upper Jurassic
Jm Meta-sediments. Chiefly Mariposa formation—slate, graywacke, etc.
Jmv Meta-volcanics. Chiefly Logtown Ridge meta-andesite

Jurassic and/or Triassic
JᴙM Milton formation—tuff, red slate, quartzite, limestone, and conglomerate

Jurassic to Paleozoic
mv Meta-volcanics of uncertain age

PALEOZOIC
Carboniferous
Cc Calaveras formation—micaschist, phyllite, quartzite, clay slate, argillite, etc.
ls Calaveras limestone

Note—Blank pattern box indicates rock type is not shown on map.

MAP SYMBOLS
▪ Lode and drift mines
▲ Placer and hydraulic (hyd) (Mine names in red)
⟋ Highway 49
[331] Historical markers
⚲ Town buildings and roads

MAP SYMBOLS FOR BUILDING STONE
[A] Adobe
[G] Granite, granodiorite
[GR] Greenstone (meta-andesite)
[L] Limestone
[R] Rhyolite tuff
[SC] Schist
[SP] Serpentine and talc schist
[SL] Slate
[SS] Tuffaceous sandstone
[ST] Soapstone
[U] Unclassified rock
⊗ Quarry site

SCALE
1 0 1 2 Miles

To Coulterville
EXCHEQUER RESERVOIR
VIRGINIA
summit el. 2050
RED BANK
Bagby el. 816
HELL HOLLOW
PINETREE & JOSEPHINE
view el. 2225
YELLOWSTONE
Bear Valley el. 2008
el. 4199 Bullion Mtn
MT. GAINES
GOLD HILL
Mt. Ophir (ghost)
OPHIR
PRINCETON Mt. Bullion el. 2134
MARIPOSA el. 2000
MERCED RIVER
BEAR VALLEY
to Hornitos
to Yosemite
to Merced

opened about 1850 and were among the earliest of the lode mines. As the veins outcrop on the flanks of a ridge of considerable height, they have been worked largely by tunnels and winzes rather than deep shafts. None of the workings extend lower than 800 feet from the tunnel levels. Some of the veins have been traced for 1200 feet along their strike. Production records on these mines are incomplete, but the total figure for both mines is in excess of $2,679,000. Prominent exposures of veins of the Mother Lode system can be seen in roadcuts in the vicinity of the Pine Tree and Josephine mines. A narrow belt of serpentine discontinuously parallels the Mother Lode fault east of the vein system. Between the Pine Tree and Josephine mines and the bed of the Merced River, the highway drops down rather abruptly across a typical section of the Mariposa formation. The rocks are mainly black slate with interbedded lenses of black, arkosic sandstone. The sandstone contains fragments of slate which are probably re-worked Mariposa material. The slates weather to a tan or grayish buff as they approach the soil mantle. Just before the road crosses the Merced River, the Mariposa is exposed in fault contact with serpentine. Serpentine has been sheared into the Mariposa at some points along this contact. Calaveras meta-sediments lie to the east of the serpentine belt.

The site of the hamlet of Benton Mills, now known as Bagby, lies just across the Merced River. A stamp mill which processed gold ore from Frémont's mines above was situated there. None of the old buildings remain although foundations of some can still be located. The Yosemite Valley Railroad once passed through Bagby but only the road-bed now remains. The tracks were removed during World War II.

North from Bagby for a distance of over six miles, Highway 49 winds up a steep slope through a barren area of serpentine and related basic and ultra-basic rocks. Serpentine ordinarily is not a favorable medium for supporting plant life although some species grow luxuriantly on it. Vegetation here is exceedingly sparse and consists principally of California holly and chemise with an occasional digger pine. The serpentine series of rocks invaded the basement sedimentary series in late Jurassic time intruding Paleozoic and Mesozoic rocks alike. The body of serpentine north of Bagby is one of the largest areas of this type of rock to be found along Highway 49.

Slightly less than two miles beyond the summit of the Bagby grade, the highway crosses the eastern border of serpentine and continues along the contact of serpentine and Calaveras rocks for a distance of about a mile. The first good exposures of the Calaveras to be seen northbound along Highway 49 are exposed there. These outcrops consist mainly of weathered tan mica schist and phyllite both of which somewhat resemble weathered Mariposa slate. They have, however, suffered a much greater degree of metamorphism, being schistose rather than slaty.

A short distance north of the summit of the Bagby grade, 3.8 miles from Bagby, a narrow dirt road from the Virginia mine leads off to the west. The Virginia mine was one of the earliest patented claims in Mariposa County and has been worked on a small scale over a very long period. The mine is 1300 feet deep on the incline and the wall rocks are Calaveras schist, Logtown Ridge greenstone, and serpentine. Records are incomplete but known production is in excess of $660,000.

A distance of 1.7 miles north of the Bagby summit, the highway crosses several dikes of an unusual grayish white rock known variously as albitite, soda syenite, and albite granophyre. Intrusive bodies of this rock are also found in many places to the east of Moccasin Creek. The rock is medium to fine grained with aplitic and porphyritic phases. It is composed mainly of the soda feldspar albite plus variable amounts of soda-rich minerals such as riebeckite and aegirite. The latter two are not present in the dikes crossing Highway 49 but are present in some of the Moccasin Creek outcrops.

A red brick furnace and chimney and a concrete foundation are all that remain of the boiler house and other buildings of the Mary Harrison mine. These are located on a knoll to the west of Highway 49, 1.8 miles south of Coulterville. The Mary Harrison was discovered sometime before 1867 and was operated for a considerable period prior to 1895 by the Cook Estate. In 1895, the mines of the Cook Estate passed into the ownership of the Merced Gold Mining Company which is responsible for most of the recorded production. This was well in excess of $330,000. The mine was worked to a depth of 1200 feet by shaft and winze. Most of the workings were in the dolomite-ankerite-mariposite-quartz rock which forms a very broad zone along this part of the Mother Lode. The mine has not been operated since 1903.

Immediately north of the ruins of the Mary Harrison, the highway has been cut through the main part of the Mother Lode vein system. This locality is easily accessible and is an excellent place to observe the minerals which are associated with gold ores. Beautifully banded rocks composed of mariposite (chrome mica), white quartz, and carbonate minerals, such as dolomite, ankerite, and calcite, can be collected there. Talc schist is present in some places—probably derived by the shearing of serpentine. The gold ore itself consists of gold bearing iron pyrites, usually somewhat oxidized.

Another excellent exposure of the veins of the Mother Lode is in the vicinity of Maxwell Creek bridge two tenths of a mile south of Coulterville. Many invasions of vein material along the same line of weakness can readily be seen in these exposures. The white silica-carbonate vein rocks are accentuated, in many places by rust-colored zones which mark the positions of sulfide-bearing gold horizons. Other yellowish-brown zones are made up of a leached, pulverized vein material which represents

FIG. 3. Morgan stope on Carson Hill, Calaveras County; looking south across the town of Carson Hill.

FIG. 4.   Jackson Butte, a volcanic neck of andesite rising above the dissected Eocene surface. View from the western outskirts of the town of Mokelumne Hill.

FIG. 5. An old etching depicting an arrastre, a crude rocker (right center), and gold pan in operation. Gold was freed from its ore by placing the ore on the floor of the flat-bottomed arrastre and dragging the large muller stones over it by horse or mule power. The muller stones were chained to a bar which revolved about a central pivot, power being applied from the end of the bar. *From an original etching loaned by Walter W. Bradley.*

FIG. 6. Looking northeast toward mine buildings of Sixteen-to-One mine at Alleghany. *Photo by C. V. Averill.*

FIG. 8. Drill cores of serpentine taken during the sinking of the 1000-foot Idaho No. 2 shaft of the Idaho-Maryland mine at Grass Valley. *Photo by W. O. Jenkins.*

FIG. 7. Doodlebug dredge in operation near the Calaveras Cement Company plant south of San Andreas. *Photo by Olaf P. Jenkins.*

FIG. 9. Abandoned wheels at Jackson Gate which were once used to lift tailings from the Kennedy mine over the hill to a tailings disposal area. These are 68 feet in diameter and were equipped with 176 buckets each.

FIG. 10. Volcanic bombs weathering from tuff on Black Creek near Copperopolis, Calaveras County. *Photo by Olaf P. Jenkins.*

FIG. 12. Lit-par-lit or injection gneiss in Agua Fria meta-sediments along Owens Creek, Mariposa County. *Photo by Olaf P. Jenkins.*

FIG. 11. Aplite dikes cutting Jurassic meta-sediments in Owens Creek canyon, Mariposa County. *Photo by Olaf P. Jenkins.*

FIG. 13. Lit-par-lit or injection gneiss in meta-sediments along Owens Creek, Mariposa County. *Photo by Olaf P. Jenkins.*

FIG. 15.   "Natural Bridge," a limestone cave, situated between Columbia and Vallecito, through which Coyote Creek runs. *Photo by Olaf P. Jenkins.*

FIG. 14.   Marble quarry north of Columbia, Tuolumne County, located on a side road to the east of the Columbia-Parrot Ferry road. *Photo by Olaf P. Jenkins.*

FIG. 16.   Mine buildings of the United States Lime Products Company lime plant at El Dorado. *Photo by Olaf P. Jenkins.*

intra-mineral or post-mineral movement along the Mother Lode fault system.

The town of Coulterville is situated in a small valley which is at about the same elevation as Bear Valley. Coulterville was founded about 1850 and was the center of a placer and gold quartz mining district which embraced the Malvina, Louisa, Potosi, Champion, and Tyro mines as well as the Mary Harrison. Many fine old buildings still remain including one built and operated by Chinese. An old mine locomotive and other pieces of early day mining equipment are on exhibit directly across the highway from Division of Highways Historical Monument 332.

COULTERVILLE TO CHINESE CAMP—MAP 2

Between Coulterville and Moccasin Creek canyon, Highway 49 passes over a rough region of serpentine and greenstone resembling the terrain north of Bagby. The principal features of scenic and geologic interest along this part of the route are the many white-tipped comb-ridges which mark the surface trace of the Mother Lode quartz veins. This series of quartz exposures was named the Peñon Blanco or white cliff by Spanish Californians. Although the long white walls are hardly tall enough to be considered cliffs, the name has persisted through the years. The weather-resistant quartz has kept the softer country rock, which forms the flanks of the ridges, from being obliterated by erosion. The best views of the Peñon Blanco may be had at a sharp bend in the highway 3.2 miles north of Coulterville, and again at the divide which marks the boundary between Mariposa and Tuolumne Counties, about five miles northwest of Coulterville.

Two-tenths of a mile below the horseshoe bend where Highway 49 drops to the level of Moccasin Creek, the serpentines end against the Mariposa slate. The latter lies in a deep synclinal trough which is disrupted on both eastern and western sides by faults. The Mother Lode thrust-fault system, which lies to the east of the syncline is a broad mineralized zone which in places reaches a width of more than 180 feet. Along the western fault contract, the Peñon Blanco or Logtown Ridge andesite agglomerate has been sheared into the Mariposa slate in many places.

At the Moccasin Creek dam and powerhouse of the city of San Francisco, an unpaved road joins Highway 49 which connects with the old placer mining district of Big Oak Flat. Big Oak Flat can also be reached via Highway 120 which crosses Highway 49 2.2 miles farther north. The placers of Big Oak Flat together with the adjoining Deer Flat and Groveland districts are credited with production in excess of $25,000,000. A few miles northeast of Big Oak Flat in the vicinity of Soulsbyville, several highly productive mines are located in what is known as the East Belt. The East Belt roughly parallels the main Mother Lode about five miles to the east of it. Veins of this belt tend to be discontinuous and much narrower than the main Mother Lode system and cut granodiorite or rocks close to it rather than meta-sediments and meta-volcanics. The most productive mines in the Soulsbyville vicinity were the Soulsby, with a production of $5,500,000, and the Black Oak with a production of $3,500,000.

A short distance beyond the intersection of Highways 49 and 120, the former crosses the Tuolumne River and continues into Jacksonville along the northwest bank of the river. This is the most scenic part of the southern third of Highway 49. There are good picnic spots along the river, several areas suitable for water sports, and the only eating places between Coulterville and Jacksonville.

Good exposures of greenstone and schists of the Calaveras formation can be seen in road cuts at the south abutment of the Tuolumne River bridge and westward along the roadbed of the Hetch-Hetchy Valley Railroad to the serpentine contact. Calaveras rocks are also exposed in roadcuts along Highway 49 from the bridge to the Harriman mine. The latter is located close to the highway 1.8 miles southeast of Jacksonville, and the headframe, sheet metal buildings, and mine dumps are very conspicuous at the roadside. Considerable capital was invested in this mine but no great production was ever recorded. With the exception of the Eagle-Shawmut, few mines in the Jacksonville district contained ore of sufficient grade to warrant major development. The gold values are disseminated through the wall rock in association with pyrite in what is locally called gray ore.

Less than half a mile southwest of Jacksonville and a short distance west of the junction of Woods Creek with the Tuolumne River, the abutments of old Moffats bridge can be seen jutting out into the Tuolumne River. The vicinity of Moffats bridge and the adjacent Hetch-Hetchy Valley Railroad cuts present good exposures of the Mariposa formation in which fossils are found. These occur in a conglomerate and were first described by H. W. Turner in the 1880's. The fossils include cephalopod and pelecypod molluscs of upper Jurassic age which correspond to Oxfordian stage fossils of Europe. Fossil leaves are also present. West from Moffats bridge, the Tuolumne River has cut directly across a 2500 foot ridge of agglomerate and serpentine. This represents a vertical downcutting at the edge of the gorge of more than 1800 feet.

Jacksonville, founded in 1848 and named for Colonel Alden Jackson, was a supply and amusement center for the mines along Moccasin and Woods Creeks. There is little or no mining activity there now. A paved road from Jacksonville connects with Jamestown via Stent and Quartz.

The extensive dumps and large mine buildings of the Eagle-Shawmut mine are located less than two miles northwest of Jacksonville at the foot of the Shawmut grade. This is one of many major gold mines along the Mother Lode which have been forced to shut down because of wartime limitations on gold mining and postwar high operating costs. The Eagle-Shawmut has many miles of workings and has produced huge tonnages of low grade ore. The total vertical depth of the mine via shaft and winze is about 3550 feet from the surface outcrop. The main shaft dips at an angle which averages 65° and has been entered for many years from adit number two. Ores in the mine consist of auriferous quartz, gold bearing massive iron sulfides, and gold bearing ankeritized country rock. The mine was opened at a very early date, being a consolidation of the old Eagle and Shawmut claims. However, most of the extensive workings were driven since the turn of the century. The Eagle-Shawmut has a recorded production of approximately $7,500,000. After passing the Eagle-Shawmut mine, Highway 49 winds up the narrow Shawmut grade to Chinese Camp. The summit of the grade affords an excellent northwesterly view of the flat surface of Table Mountain lava flow. The road-cuts along the Shawmut grade expose Mariposa slates and green Logtown Ridge agglomerates. After passing the divide, the highway crosses gently rolling country in which there are few exposures of basement rocks.

Chinese Camp was a placer-mining center first settled by Chinese laborers in 1849. Ruins of structures built in the fifties still remain together with a few more modern dwellings. Piles of soil and gravel which were turned over in frantic search for gold can still be seen in every gulch. These gravels are reworked remnants of pre-existing Eocene and later Tertiary deposits most of which have since been stripped off by erosion.

The prominent flat surface of Tuolumne Table Mountain lies $2\frac{1}{2}$ miles northwest of Chinese Camp. Though appearing as a table when viewed from the road, it looks more like a sinuous river when seen from the air; and that is what it is—a fossil river—an ancient stream canyon cut in a broad flat sheet of volcanic ash but filled to the brim by a viscous flow of dark colored lava extending for 60 miles from the high Sierra Nevada to its terminus against a bluff of sedimentary andesitic beds near Knights Ferry. As the Sierra Nevada mass was raised and tilted slightly westward, the softer ash beds were largely washed away by erosion, leaving the very resistant lava flow high and dry as a dominating table. In places the stream which originally cut the channel later occupied by the lava, cut clear through the ash beds and even into the tops of some underlying buried hill tops of bed rock. In other places where the ash beds lay deep beneath the lava stream, the pre-volcanic topographic surface was preserved. It is in the pre-volcanic stream courses under this older ash cover that the older gold placers were discovered and mined, as in the old New York tunnel. The younger channel of Table Mountain was largely barren of gold.

The resistant latite lava flow of Table Mountain, which is probably of late Pliocene age, has thus protected some of the earlier softer Tertiary deposits from obliteration by erosion. The latite lava capping is flat-topped, with vertical cliffs along the edge, showing columnar joining of the rock. Tuffs and mudflows are exposed under or close to the base of the cliffs. The latite closely resembles a porphyritic olivine basalt, the potash feldspars being entirely confined to the groundmass. Some plagioclase crystals, however, are more than an inch long.

Andesitic tuffs, gravels and boulders can be seen lying directly beneath the latite at Mountain Pass, where the ancient stream channel, now occupied by the lava, cut a V-shaped gorge in the andesite cobble deposit. At this point is a watering place known as Mountain Springs, located less than half a mile from the junction of Highways 49 and 108 or $4\frac{1}{2}$ miles from Chinese Camp. An area suitable for picnicking adjoins the spring and water fountain. The water flows from the ancient ash-covered bed of the Tertiary channel.

The bouldery andesite is known as the Mehrten formation and is well exposed on the road southeast of Mountain Pass. It lies stratigraphically above the Eocene quartz gravels which are present lying on bedrock. Some of the earlier quartz gravels, however, a mile northeast of Mountain Pass occur intermixed with the andesite cobble. These deposits represent post-Eocene channels which cut through the earlier Eocene deposits and robbed them of their gravels and also their gold.

The earliest gold-bearing stream channels, Eocene in age, often followed the strike of bedrock, cutting gutters and depositing gold nuggets. The andesite cobble was spread far and wide, covering both the bedrock and the Eocene channels. The much later latite lava flow took the course of a prominent post-andesite stream gorge and filled it to the brim. Where drift mining discovered the deep Eocene quartz gravel channels, rich placers were found; but where the mines encountered post-Eocene channels cut only through the barren volcanic ash, disappointment was the result. For this reason only a few of the drift mines which pass under Table Mountain were successful; many others were a disappointment.

CHINESE CAMP TO ALTAVILLE—MAP 3

The highway, from Mountain Springs and on into Jamestown, more or less parallels the trend of Table Mountain. Bedrock exposures are poor because of the low relief, there being few good outcrops until Woods Crossing is reached. The Mariposa slates appear briefly from beneath the Tertiary gravel and andesite series, and then are faulted off against a thin belt of Logtown Ridge metavolcanics. This contact is close to the junction of the Montezuma cutoff and Highway 49 about $2\frac{1}{2}$ miles northeast of Mountain Springs. From that point to Woods Crossing the basement rocks are principally serpentine and related gabbro-diorite.

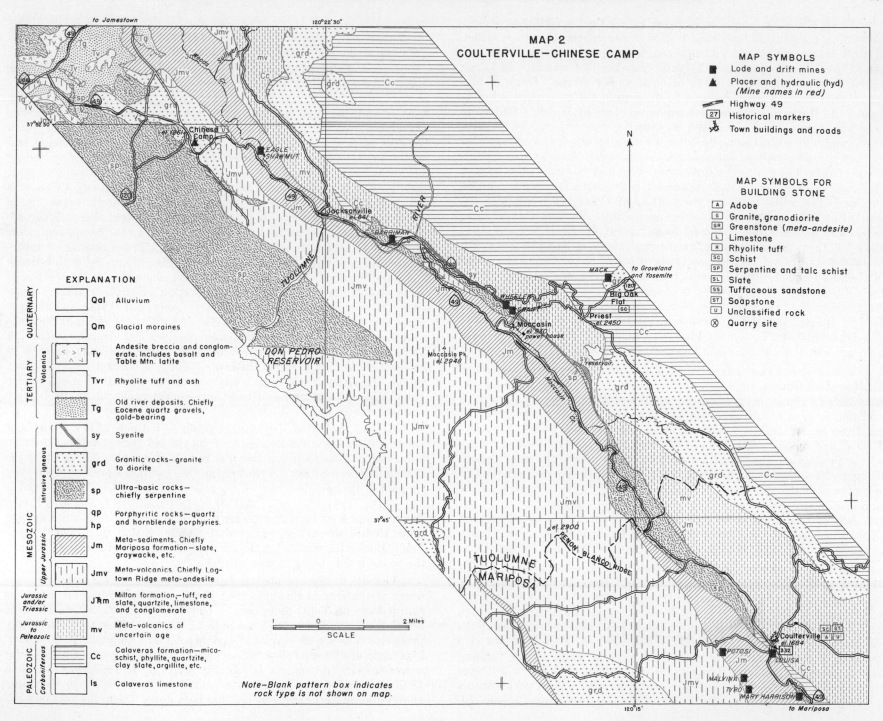

MAP 2
COULTERVILLE—CHINESE CAMP

MAP SYMBOLS
■ Lode and drift mines
▲ Placer and hydraulic (hyd)
   (Mine names in red)
▱ Highway 49
27 Historical markers
Town buildings and roads

MAP SYMBOLS FOR
BUILDING STONE
A Adobe
G Granite, granodiorite
GR Greenstone (meta-andesite)
L Limestone
R Rhyolite tuff
SC Schist
SP Serpentine and talc schist
SL Slate
SS Tuffaceous sandstone
ST Soapstone
U Unclassified rock
⊗ Quarry site

EXPLANATION

QUATERNARY
Qal Alluvium
Qm   Glacial moraines

TERTIARY
Volcanics
Tv   Andesite breccia and conglomerate. Includes basalt and Table Mtn. latite
Tvr Rhyolite tuff and ash
Tg   Old river deposits. Chiefly Eocene quartz gravels, gold-bearing

MESOZOIC
Intrusive igneous
sy   Syenite
grd Granitic rocks—granite to diorite
sp   Ultra-basic rocks—chiefly serpentine
qp
hp   Porphyritic rocks—quartz and hornblende porphyries.

Upper Jurassic
Jm   Meta-sediments. Chiefly Mariposa formation—slate, graywacke, etc.
Jmv Meta-volcanics Chiefly Logtown Ridge meta-andesite

Jurassic and/or Triassic
JRm Milton formation—tuff, red slate, quartzite, limestone, and conglomerate

Jurassic to Paleozoic
mv   Meta-volcanics of uncertain age

PALEOZOIC
Carboniferous
Cc   Calaveras formation—mica-schist, phyllite, quartzite, clay slate, argillite, etc.
ls   Calaveras limestone

SCALE
1   0   1   2 Miles

Note—Blank pattern box indicates rock type is not shown on map.

to Jamestown
120°22′30″
37°02′30″
Chinese Camp el. 1261
EAGLE SHAWMUT
Jacksonville el. 841
HARRIMAN
TUOLUMNE RIVER
DON PEDRO RESERVOIR
MACK
to Groveland and Yosemite
WHEELER
Big Oak Flat
Priest el. 2450
Moccasin el. 930 power house
Moccasin Pk. el. 2948
reservoir.
Moccasin Cr.
37°45′
el. 2900
PENON BLANCO RIDGE
TUOLUMNE
MARIPOSA
el. 2900
Coulterville el. 1684
POTOSI
LOUISA
MALVINA
TYRO
MARY HARRISON
to Mariposa
120°15′

Woods Crossing, now a cross roads rather than a ford, has several interesting features. It is marked by a sign commemorating the passing of Bret Harte and Mark Twain through the gold country which was placed there by the Tuolumne County Chamber of Commerce in honor of two authors who did much to bring the color of the "Days of 49" before the public. A short distance to the west of the crossing, the buildings of the Harvard mine can be seen on the slope of Whiskey Hill. This mine was discovered in 1850 and was worked continuously until 1916. The prominent quartz-ankerite outcrops close to which the ore lay also outcrop conspicuously in the long roadcut between Woods Crossing and Woods Creek. The multiple nature of the vein system can readily be seen there and some minerals, such as the attractive mica mariposite, can be obtained. The veins lie along the contact of Calaveras schist and the serpentine body mentioned in preceding paragraphs. The Harvard has two shafts but only one was used to any great extent. The main shaft has a 700 foot vertical drop and then turns at an angle of 58° to a depth of 1850 feet. The veins have been worked for 1500 feet along the strike of the Mother Lode. Post-mineral faulting has displaced the ore shoots from 8 to 20 feet in some places. A 60 stamp mill employing 1200 pound stamps is on the property. Some recent development work has been done, but no attempt at major production has taken place in recent years. The Harvard has a known production of $2,036,697 but no records were kept prior to 1897, and a much larger figure is probable.

To the east of Highway 49, a road leads off to the old mining camps of Stent and Quartz. Both can also be reached from roads out of Jacksonville and Jamestown, being about 2½ miles south of the latter. In addition to local placering, Stent and Quartz are famous for a group of hardrock mines the best known of which are the App, Dutch, Sweeney, Heslep, and Jumper. The Jumper has recently been rehabilitated but no recent production has yet been reported. It is a consolidation of the old Jumper, New Era, and Golden Rule claims, the combined production of which is more than $3,000,000. The presence of the gold tellurides petzite and hessite has been reported from the Jumper. Combined production of the App and Heslep has been placed at more than $1,742,000 and that of the Dutch and Sweeney at approximately $2,118,000. These were fairly deep mines, the Dutch having a vertical depth of about 2070 feet.

Beyond the Mother Lode vein exposures at Woods Crossing, a very thick section of Calaveras rocks begins. The Calaveras formation can be seen on both sides of Highway 49 from Jamestown to well beyond the Calaveras River bridge. The rocks are mica schists, phyllites, limestones, and green metavolcanics. Several more or less parallel branches of the Mother Lode traverse the Jamestown-San Andreas strip, and the vein systems tend to finger out into the wall rocks in many places, forming networks of veinlets or stringers. Some of the stringer lodes were extremely auriferous and were responsible for the famous pocket mines of Rawhide and Jackass Hill. Some of the ore bodies on Carson Hill were of this type. It is probable that a great deal of high grade ore of this nature was eroded off during Cretaceous and Eocene time to form the fabulously rich placers of Columbia and Shaws Flat.

Jamestown or Jimtown, as it is familiarly called, is a still thriving community with a history dating from 1848. It long has been the supply center for a great many small mining camps, and the major workings at Stent and Quartz lie nearby to the south. A veritable network of roads branch off from Highway 49 in the vicinity of Jamestown all of which traverse areas of mining and geological interest. The road to Stent and Quartz has been mentioned in previous paragraphs. Another one leading off northwesterly from the center of town crosses Table Mountain, goes through the ghost town of Rawhide, and rejoins Highway 49 about a mile east of Tuttletown. This route crosses Table Mountain close to the old Tuttletown-Jamestown segment of the abandoned Sierra Railroad. A closeup view of the latite lava cap and underlying tuffaceous sediments can be seen in the railroad cut close to the road. The columnar structure of the latite is particularly conspicuous. The rim, or contact with bedrock along the old slope of the fossil stream bank, shows in the old weathered surface of the covered schist, a cross section of surface hillside creep which has been preserved since the lava covered it. Close by this spot to the north is the location of the old New York Tunnel which drifted into gold bearing gravels following a channel which led the miners beneath Table Mountain. The gravels lie beneath rhyolitic lake beds, covered by andesite cobble, all of which the lava of Table Mountain spanned like a bridge. The New York tunnel was one of the few drift mines under Table Mountain which could boast any considerable profit. Its heyday was prior to 1868.

West of the Table Mountain crossing, a distance of seven-tenths of a mile, the Rawhide road joins one from the old Omega mining district. Southeast of this road junction the red sheet metal stamp mill of the Omega mine can be seen. Although the Omega mine has never been very successful, the mill has been in operation for much of the time and is one of the few stamp mills still in operation along the Mother Lode. The mill site is of further geologic interest because a post-latite normal fault, Pleistocene in age, passes almost under it and then cuts through Table Mountain, displacing the lava cap a vertical distance of 60 feet, the western side being higher than the eastern.

The site of the old mining camp of Rawhide lies a short distance north of the Omega-Rawhide road junction almost due west from the railroad cut on Table Mountain. A body of pure antigorite serpentine lies to the south and west of the town of Rawhide. This was extensively prospected during the war as a possible source of magnesium. The Rawhide mine, also located close to the town of Rawhide, was one of the most successful early day mines. It was very active up to 1867; was idle until 1891; and had a very productive period up to 1905. Since then only pocket mining in the old workings has been done. The veins are typically

FIG. 17. Hummocky limestone bedrock at Columbia. View is northeast toward St. Anne's Church. More than $17,000,000 in gold was taken from this surface during the '50's

FIG. 19. Looking northeast toward eroded face of old hydraulic pit at North Columbia. Crossbedding can be seen in the upper left hand part of the picture. *Photo by Olaf P. Jenkins.*

FIG. 18. Rolling exhumed Eocene land surface as seen to the northwest of Kelsey, El Dorado County.

FIG. 20. Hummocky limestone bedrock at Shaws Flat, a rich placer camp much like Columbia, which lies a few miles to the northeast.

FIG. 21. View south down the North Fork of the American River from the Highway, 49 bridge at the El Dorado-Placer County line. The abandoned Pacific Portland Cement Company railroad bridge may be seen in the background. The beveled bedrock in the right foreground is a green meta-volcanic of doubtful age.

FIG. 23. Adit and buildings of the Pacific Minerals Company slate mine on the South Fork of the American River two miles north of Placerville.

FIG. 22. Potholes worn in granodiorite bedrock in the streambed of the South Fork of the Yuba River immediately east of the Highway 49 bridge.

FIG. 24. Looking northwest toward Tuolumne Table Mountain from the vicinity of the Omega and Rawhide mines. Dumps and buildings of the Rawhide mine may be seen in the upper left part of the picture. *Photo by Olaf P. Jenkins.*

CHINESE CAMP–ALTAVILLE   MAP 3

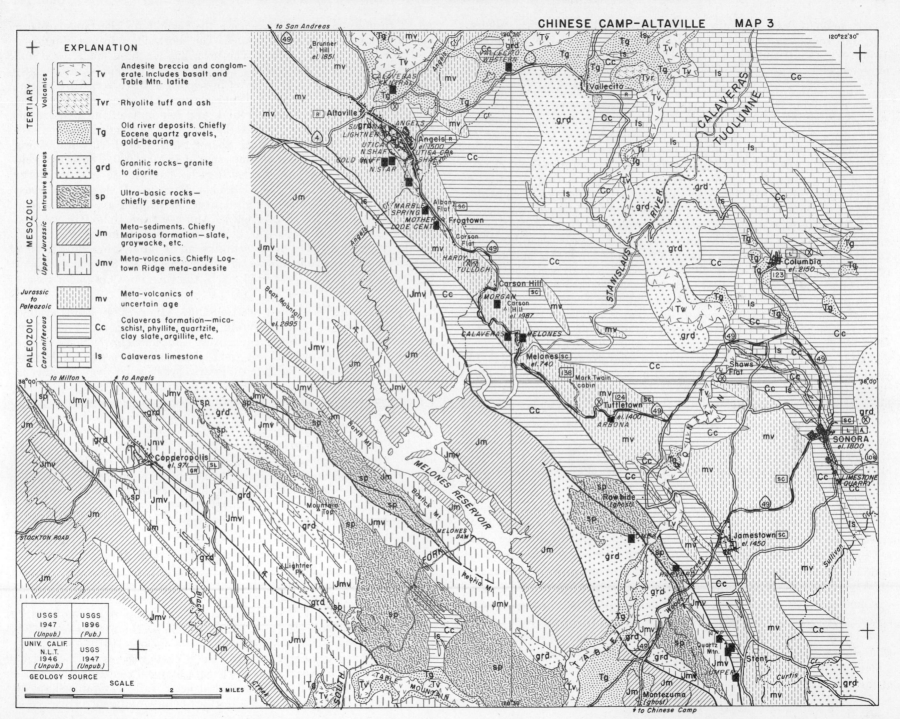

EXPLANATION

TERTIARY — Volcanics

	Tv	Andesite breccia and conglomerate. Includes basalt and Table Mtn. latite
	Tvr	Rhyolite tuff and ash
	Tg	Old river deposits. Chiefly Eocene quartz gravels, gold-bearing

MESOZOIC — Intrusive igneous

| | grd | Granitic rocks – granite to diorite |
| | sp | Ultra-basic rocks – chiefly serpentine |

Upper Jurassic

| | Jm | Meta-sediments. Chiefly Mariposa formation – slate, graywacke, etc. |
| | Jmv | Meta-volcanics. Chiefly Logtown Ridge meta-andesite |

Jurassic to Paleozoic

| | mv | Meta-volcanics of uncertain age |

PALEOZOIC — Carboniferous

| | Cc | Calaveras formation – mica-schist, phyllite, quartzite, clay slate, argillite, etc. |
| | ls | Calaveras limestone |

GEOLOGY SOURCE

| USGS 1947 (Unpub.) | USGS 1896 (Pub.) |
| UNIV. CALIF. N.L.T. 1946 (Unpub.) | USGS 1947 (Unpub.) |

SCALE
1 0 1 2 3 MILES

quartz-ankerite rock containing both free gold and gold bearing sulfides. The wall rocks are Calaveras schist and serpentine. The total depth is 1845 feet via shaft and winze. Probable production is in the neighborhood of $6,000,000.

Four-tenths of a mile north of Jamestown a road which leads to Shaws Flat joins Highway 49. Shaws Flat is accessible from Sonora and Columbia also. The town was founded in 1850 but the rich placer diggins of the Shaws Flat-Sonora district were discovered in the summer of 1848. As at Columbia, which is but a few miles to the north, the Calaveras limestone underlies most of the diggings and has an extremely rough, hummocky, crevassed, potholed, surface, caused by surface leaching of ground water and probably accomplished, for the most part, since the gold was deposited. Much of the gold was found in the red, weathered clay of the limestone, and not directly on the bedrock. Some of the Eocene gravels which once covered the limestone surface can be seen, but they are scarce because they were probably stripped off this surface by erosion long before the days of 49. Although exceedingly rich, the Shaws Flat deposits were very shallow and were soon worked out. The source of the gold from these early rich placers may well have been close by; for north of Sonora on the road to this area is a hillside covered with early pocket mines. No accurate breakdown on the production of Shaws Flat, Whimtown, and other diggings in the Shaws Flat vicinity are available, but it is probable that part of the $87,000,000 credited to Columbia came from diggings to the south. Some of the channels of this district were followed partly under Table Mountain, separated from it by deposits of andesitic cobble.

Between Jamestown and Sonora, the countryside becomes more hilly and is rather well forested. There are several resorts and picnic spots along the highway and several nice stands of pine timber. The rocks along the way are Calaveras schists and greenstones of no particular interest.

Sonora, one of the larger foothill towns and county seat of Tuolumne County, was founded in 1848 by Spanish Americans. It is a flourishing and attractive town with its yellow frame County Courthouse and rustic red St. James Church. Sonora boasted a newspaper as early as 1850. The Holden Chispa nugget which weighed over 28 pounds was taken from diggings within the present city limits. An excellent collection of gold specimens may be seen at McKibbens Mountain Cafe on the main street of town. Historical Marker 139, placed there by the American Automobile Association and State Division of Highways commemorates St. James Church, and the Tuolumne County Chamber of Commerce has erected a monument to the early pioneers of the city located at the divided part of the main street through town. Sonora is the gateway to the Pine Crest resorts and Sonora Pass in the High Sierra.

Two miles northwest of Sonora, the turnoff for the famous placer mining camp of Columbia is located. The short side trip to Columbia is well worth the traveler's time. The town has not been modernized and is in a fair state of preservation. The vicinity of Columbia has recently been made a state park. St. Ann's Church, a red brick structure located to the south of town, has all of its old charm. The search for gold is said to have stopped at the church grounds and remnants of the gold gravels supposedly lie untouched beneath the church. The rough limestone bedrock, which is much like that at Shaws Flat, is credited with having caught and held gold to the fabulous sum of $87,000,000. Few if any gold placers of similar area have yielded so rich a harvest! Several very large nuggets were taken from the Columbia diggings. A slab-shaped mass found on Knapp's Ranch weighed over 50 pounds avoirdupois, and $8,500 in gold was recovered from it. Another from Gold Hill weighed 362 troy ounces valued at $6,500. Two others were valued at $5,265 and $5,000 respectively. The town contains many interesting buildings, a local-color museum, and a sweetshop par-excellence. State Division of Highways Historical Marker 123 marks the turn onto Columbia's main street.

After leaving the vicinity of Columbia, Highway 49 bends around the northern end of Table Mountain and follows along its western base for about two miles before turning west into Tuttletown. Some of the gravels in the creek beds of this vicinity are being worked for gold by small dragline dredges. Tuttletown, located seven miles from Sonora via Highway 49, was first settled by Mormons in 1848, and was originally called Mormon Camp. James M. Tuttle, whose name the town now bears, arrived considerably later than the first Mormons. A fairly well preserved stone structure dating from 1852 is one of the few relics remaining in old Tuttletown. Division of Highways Historical Marker 124 is located near this spot. The headframe and red sheet iron buildings of the Arbona mine are located close to the highway near the center of Tuttletown. The mine has a 600-foot inclined shaft in schist country rock. Production from this mine has not been extensive and there has been no major exploitation since 1909. Some pocket gold was recovered from it during the early thirties.

State Division of Highways Historical Marker 138, one mile from Tuttletown, is close to the turnoff to Jackass Hill. Jackass Hill was once famous for its "pocket" gold mines and has since been made a shrine to to the memory of Mark Twain who stayed there with the Gillis Brothers for an indefinite period. The present Mark Twain cabin is a reconstructed replica of old cabins in the area and is not the original Gillis cabin. No production figure is available for the mines on Jackass Hill, known generally as the Chileno group, but some of the pockets were exceedingly rich. The gold occurs in quartz and carbonate stringers cutting Calaveras schist. The Jackass Hill mines produced beautifully crystallized specimens of gold as well as the gold tellurides petzite and calaverite.

A mile and a half northwest of the Mark Twain historical markers, the mine dumps and building foundation of the Norwegian mine can be seen to the north of the highway. The Norwegian is really on the northwest slope of Jackass Hill although it is some distance from the pocket mines near the Mark Twain cabin. This mine has been worked discontinuously in a small way since 1851, but is now idle. The ore was in pockets and ore minerals included gold, pyrite, chalcopyrite, galena, petzite, and small quantities of other tellurides. The total recorded production is only $131,000 but considerably more was undoubtedly produced of which there is no record. The Norwegian mine is of interest principally because the notorious outlaw Black Bart was caught as a result of a fracas involving a stage carrying Norwegian mine gold. Bart is supposed to have dropped during the holdup the handkerchief by which he was traced to his lair in San Francisco.

Beyond the Norwegian mine, Highway 49 drops into the canyon of the Stanislaus River, and crosses the latter at Robinsons Ferry, immediately south of the town of Melones. During high water, the canyon bottom is flooded by the lake which backs up behind the Melones Dam, located more than seven miles downstream. The most recent highwater mark can be seen on the canyon walls as a line of dirt and debris. The bridge at Robinsons Ferry is at the Tuolumne-Calaveras County line, a line which follows the course of the Stanislaus in this area. Melones, situated on the north bank of the river, would be a very scenic spot were it not for the shambles of shacks and worn out mining equipment which clutter the hillside behind the town. The large 100 stamp mill and some other buildings burned in 1942 and the mine premises have badly deteriorated since then. The Melones-Carson Hill mining district has one of the most colorful histories of any along the Mother Lode and mining on Carson Hill has for the most part been a very lucrative enterprise. Although early records are incomplete, Carson Hill mines are credited with a production of more than $26,000,000. Spanish American miners found placer gold along the Stanislaus and its tributaries early in 1848. They are responsible for the name Melones, which was applied to the area because of the placer gold which resembled melon seeds. In 1850, two years after the Spanish Americans located the town of Melones, James Carson and John Hance were digging placer gold from Carson Creek. Hance is credited with the initial lode-gold discovery on Carson Hill when he followed placer gold showings uphill to their source near the massive quartz outcroppings. The Billy Mulligan gang jumped the claims and held them for nine months before being thrown off the property by court order in 1853. Little more than a year later, the largest mass of gold ever produced in California and one of the largest on record was taken from Carson Hill. It weighed 195 pounds troy which, calculated at present prices and 900 fineness, would be worth $73,710. At the time of discovery it was worth $43,534. Presence of this huge mass of gold brought business to Robinsons Ferry to the tune of $10,000 in tolls in less than six weeks!

The mines of Carson Hill are famous for the telluride minerals produced in quantity during the early decades of operation. Calaverite, hessite, petzite, and sylvanite were common minerals in Carson Hill. Melonite, a telluride of nickel, is a very rare mineral named after the town of Melones and is found in but few other parts of the world.

Two large surface workings or glory holes can be seen on Carson Hill. One is on the southwest flank of the hill 1.5 miles from Melones. This is the Calaveras cut on the Santa Cruz claim. The larger of the two is located on the north side of the hill about a mile south of the town of Carson Hill. This is the Morgan stope on the Morgan claim. The Morgan stope was exploited partly by steam shovels from the surface but most of the ore was taken out through tunnels from below. The Melones tunnel, the adit of which is close to Highway 49 just north of Melones, was the main ore-removal way from the Morgan claim. Some idea of the magnitude of the Carson Hill workings may be drawn from the tremendous size of the tailings dump to the east of Melones.

North from Melones, Highway 49 rises abruptly along the flanks of Carson Hill. There are 3.5 miles of narrow switchbacks and sinuous mountain driving between Melones and the town of Carson Hill. The road cuts on Carson Hill expose a great many quartz-carbonate stringers or veinlets which are typical of the Mother Lode mineralization on its eastern spur from Jackass Hill to Angels Camp. The main thrust fault of the Mother Lode system lies considerably to the west and was not mineralized along this sector. North from Carson Hill the route lies in rolling country which has been exploited both by placering and lode mining. Evidences of both are to be seen everywhere. Carson Flat, Frogtown, and Albany Flat were early day gold camps though little now remains at the old sites which lay close to present day Highway 49. The Mother Lode Central, Marble Spring, Harris, and Waterman mines are all located close to the highway on its west side between Carson Hill and Angels Camp. None of them has been particularly productive as compared with Carson Hill or the mines at Angels Camp. See the map which accompanies this chapter for more precise locations on these mines.

Angels Camp, 3.8 miles north of Carson Hill town, was founded in 1848 by Henry Angel. It is a modern, up-to-date town with few buildings of historical interest remaining. Although its stream placers were rich, the lodes proved richer and more permanent. Some were exploited as late as 1920. The Utica mine, which was a consolidation of the Utica, Stickles, Raspberry, and six other claims, is by far the most famous mine between Carson Hill and Jackson. Although fires and cave-ins hampered production from time to time, the Utica produced gold to the amazing total of nearly $17,000,000. The veins and hence the shafts are nearly vertical and the deepest part of the mine is 3050 feet below the surface via shaft and winze. The veins are faulted off on the south side of town and attempts to relocate the ore shoots south of the cross-fault have failed. The working shaft and adjacent stopes are located on the north side of town in an area now set aside as a city park. The depressed portion of the park is the result of the caving of the stopes beneath.

A half mile west of the Utica is the Gold Cliff mine, which was operated by the Utica Mining Company for about five years after the Utica closed down. The Gold Cliff is also a consolidation of half a dozen early-day claims. It is on the main Mother Lode fault system whereas the Utica is probably on the same east spur as are the Carson Hill ore bodies. The Gold Cliff was prospected to a depth of 2700 feet along an incline which averaged 45° in dip, but most of the ore came from above the 1900 foot level. Between the 1600 and 1700 foot levels, the ore bodies are offset to the north by a nearly horizontal fault of several hundred feet displacement. The Utica Mining Company announced a total production for the Gold Cliff of $2,834,000.

ALTAVILLE TO MOKELUMNE HILL—MAP 4

Altaville, located at the junction of Highways 49 and 4 one mile north of Angels Camp is, like its larger neighbor a modern town with but few remaining historical spots. Originally known as Cherokee Flat, Altaville was a crossroads point of supply for adjacent placer mines. A group of drift mines which has produced much placer gold is located to the east of Altaville and Angels Camp. The term drift mines is here applied to underground placer mines which reach the old buried river gravels by shafts and tunnels. The Calaveras Central, Slab Ranch, Golden River, and Vallecito Western are some of the mines located in this region, all of which entered the Central Hill gravel channel at different places on its course. This fossil stream channel lies buried about three hundred feet beneath the surface and is filled with gravel and volcanic ash. The Calaveras Central mine was being rehabilitated early in 1948, but is now closed. Its workings are very extensive and reach the buried channel on a bend in its course from west to north. Coarse gold nuggets were found directly on bedrock slate riffles where the Eocene gutters cut across and followed the structure. Huge boulders lie on the upturned edges of the slate. Rhyolitic lake bed ash containing fossil leaves lies upon this coarse gravel. Above this and filled to the surface is volcanic ash and stream gravel of all sorts.

These mines are located between Highway 4, running east from Angels Camp, and the Murphys Grade road which runs east from Altaville. The sidetrip from Altaville to Murphys and back to Angels Camp is one which no visitor to this part of the gold country should miss.

Traveling east from Altaville the quarried outcrops of grayish-tan rhyolite tuff of the Valley Springs formation can be seen in rounded hills above a surface of lesser relief. The tuff overlies the gravel channels in many places and it is beneath this material that the drift mines have been driven. The tuff has been extensively quarried for use as a building stone because of its accessibility, durability, and workable properties. The Calaveras Central mine is located on the north side of Bald Hill the turnoff to which is six-tenths of a mile east of Altaville. As seen from the south, the name Bald Hill is a misnomer, that side of the hill being brushed over. Bald Hill is the site of the famous "Calaveras Skull" hoax, perpetrated on geologist J. D. Whitney and others in the 1860's, in which an Indian skull was placed as a practical joke at the bottom of a shaft which was sunk in the Tertiary stream gravels. A few miles beyond Bald Hill the road locally known as Murphys Grade begins a gradual ascent up the park-like canyon of Angels Creek to Murphys, probably the best preserved and most beautiful of the old towns which date from the gold rush. Very little modernization has been done there. Looking down its main street with its fine old buildings and overhanging trees is like turning back the pages of history nearly a hundred years. Murphys is the starting place for Mercers Cave, a limestone cavern privately owned but open to the public, the Sheep Ranch mining district, Murphys mining district, and the High Sierra of Ebbetts Pass.

The lode mines of the Murphys district, located on Highway 4 a few miles northeast of the town of Murphys, differ from most other gold deposits in the vicinity of the Mother Lode in that the veinlets or stringers are in limestone country rock instead of in meta-volcanics or meta-clastics. The mines were discovered in 1848 but were never sensational producers.

Doubling back on Highway 4 toward Angels Camp, the hydraulic diggings of Douglas Flat are evident to the northwest of the road. This is one of the most southerly of a great series of immense hydraulic diggings which are scattered from Calaveras to southern Plumas County. Above the face of the Douglas Flat pit is a black lava-breccia cap the edges of which are fluted by weathering, but have the false appearance of columns, jointing which is characteristic of the solid lava of Table Mountain latite. The latite flow is located to the east.

Vallecito is two and a half miles southwest of Douglas Flat. At the town of Vallecito a road from Columbia joins Highway 4. This road starts north from Columbia, following the Eocene Columbia River channel, passing close to a large marble quarry in Calaveras limestone to the east, and then descending the deep and spectacular canyon of the Stanislaus River. On the way one may look up this magnificent canyon and see clearly where the river has cut through a wide belt of Calaveras limestone. Table Mountain latite shows up prominently on the north side of the canyon as well as the south, and as the road winds down through granite rock various fine scenes come into view until finally it crosses the river at Parrott Ferry. Here one should examine the outcrop of granitic rock with inclusions of earlier intruded rock bodies and then

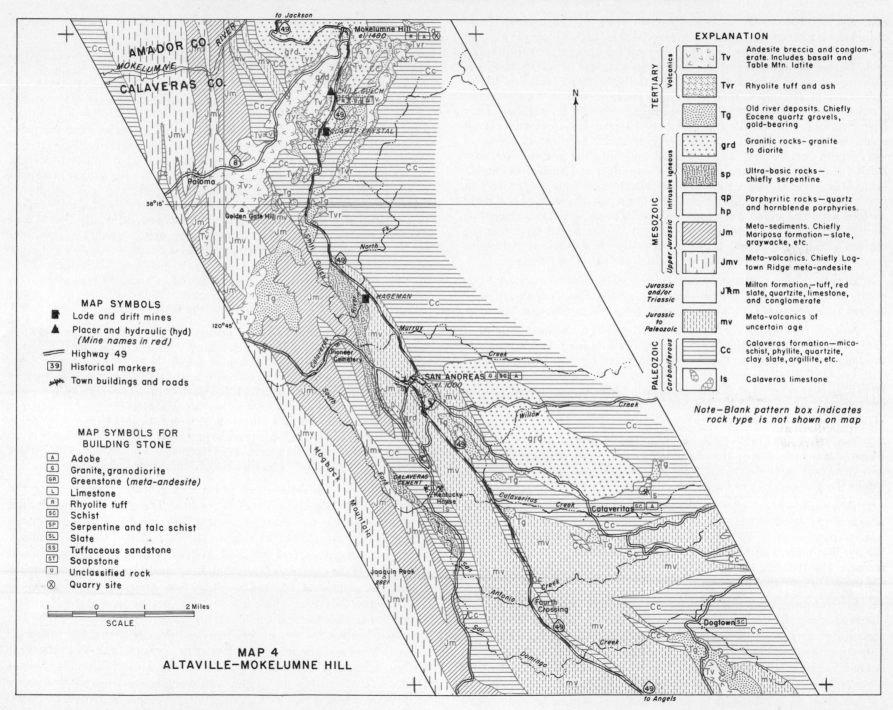

EXPLANATION

TERTIARY — Volcanics	Tv	Andesite breccia and conglomerate. Includes basalt and Table Mtn. latite
	Tvr	Rhyolite tuff and ash
	Tg	Old river deposits. Chiefly Eocene quartz gravels, gold-bearing
MESOZOIC — Intrusive igneous	grd	Granitic rocks—granite to diorite
	sp	Ultra-basic rocks—chiefly serpentine
	qp hp	Porphyritic rocks—quartz and hornblende porphyries.
MESOZOIC — Upper Jurassic	Jm	Meta-sediments. Chiefly Mariposa formation—slate, graywacke, etc.
	Jmv	Meta-volcanics. Chiefly Logtown Ridge meta-andesite
Jurassic and/or Triassic	JŦm	Milton formation,—tuff, red slate, quartzite, limestone, and conglomerate
Jurassic to Paleozoic	mv	Meta-volcanics of uncertain age
PALEOZOIC — Carboniferous	Cc	Calaveras formation—mica-schist, phyllite, quartzite, clay slate, argillite, etc.
	ls	Calaveras limestone

Note—Blank pattern box indicates rock type is not shown on map

MAP SYMBOLS

■ Lode and drift mines
▲ Placer and hydraulic (hyd)
    (Mine names in red)
— Highway 49
39 Historical markers
⟋ Town buildings and roads

MAP SYMBOLS FOR
BUILDING STONE

A Adobe
G Granite, granodiorite
GR Greenstone (*meta-andesite*)
L Limestone
R Rhyolite tuff
SC Schist
SP Serpentine and talc schist
SL Slate
SS Tuffaceous sandstone
ST Soapstone
U Unclassified rock
⊗ Quarry site

SCALE 1 0 1 2 Miles

MAP 4
ALTAVILLE-MOKELUMNE HILL

look upward 1000 feet higher to the two stubs of the severed Table Mountain latite. On the north side may be seen high up on the canyon wall the V-shaped cross-section of the lava-filled channel, cut in granitic rock. Before the uptilting of the Sierra Nevada, this lava occupying the sinuous course of what may have been the ancestral Stanislaus River, flowed across this place, then at a much lower elevation. As the Sierra Nevada block was raised and tilted slightly westward, the present newly born Stanislaus River, flowing down the Sierran slope cut and carved a canyon through the lava and underlying rocks, keeping its course as the Sierran surface rose, and cutting deeply into the granite. Not only is this lava-filled channel cut in two, but also the earlier Columbia channel is bisected. A continuation of this channel which was left just north of Columbia is again encountered on the road as it reaches the old surface after the climb out of the canyon. The road follows along this ancient channel and the edge of the present Coyote Creek canyon at the bottom of which, 300 feet lower in elevation, is a Natural Bridge or remnant of a limestone cave through which the creek now flows.

Moaning Cave, a limestone cavern privately owned but open to the public, is located on the opposite side of Coyote Creek canyon and may be seen from the road. It is also two miles from the junction in Vallecito.

As one travels west into Angels on Highway 4, the head frames of the Golden River, Vallecito Western, and Slab Ranch mines are seen to the north of Highway 4. These drift mines are now all idle and filled with water. Though the geology of the Tertiary channels is not very well known, it is possible that this Central Hill Channel may be part of the same stream system as the Columbia River Channel which was bisected by the Stanislaus River.

Two-tenths of a mile from the junction of Highways 4 and 49 in Angels Camp the site of the old chlorination plant is located. Chlorination was an early day method for recovering gold from concentrates before the process of cyanidation was discovered.

Two mining districts of considerable interest lie to the west of Altaville along Highway 4. Dumps and prospect holes of the Gold Hill pocket mining district can be seen a short distance to the north of the road. The Wagon Rut mine was the best known of the Gold Hill mines. The head-frame of the Belmont-Osborne mine is situated half a mile southwest of the Gold Hill group and can also be seen from the road.

Several interesting sidelights on the wildlife of the vicinity may be observed along the Copperopolis route. Telephone poles and fence posts are riddled by the acorn studded holes of California woodpeckers. The fence posts are further burdened by the carcasses of dozens of predatory animals which the ranchers have trapped or otherwise disposed of. It seems to be a custom of the country to exhibit "varmints" in this fashion. No less than 34 coyotes and three bobcats were strung on consecutive fence posts within a two-mile stretch on the authors' last trip through that country!

The Copperopolis copper mining district 12 miles southwest of Altaville was a major producer through both World Wars but has been idle much of the time between war periods. The North Keystone, Empire, and Keystone-Union are the principal mines of the district and are all located in town within a short distance of each other. The Copperopolis mines were discovered in 1861 and for several years thereafter were the principal producers of California copper. The upper parts of the ore bodies were very rich and the Union and Keystone mines paid huge dividends. The Copperopolis mines are on a fault system as are the Mother Lode gold mines, but the Copperopolis mines carry little gold and lack the quartz-carbonate gangue of the Mother Lode veins. The ore is of simple sulfide type, principally pyrite and chalcopyrite and is exceptionally free of base metallic elements other than copper. The massive sulfides pass into pyritic or chalcopyritic slate at peripheries of the ore shoots. The ore bodies lie in a narrow belt of hydrothermally-altered black slate of the Mariposa formation with Logtown Ridge meta-andesite agglomerate on either side. Dikes of diorite cut the Logtown Ridge in many places near Copperopolis paralleling the strike of the bedded rocks.

The town of Copperopolis, located in the center of Salt Springs Valley, has but few buildings remaining. The red brick I.O.O.F. Hall, originally built in 1862 as a church, is one of the few still in a good state of preservation. A Mr. McCarty had mined and farmed in Salt Springs Valley as early as 1852 and had prospected the copper veins for gold. Finding no gold, he paid no further attention to the copper deposits until he returned with two others in 1861 and helped to found Copperopolis. The history of Copperopolis has been one of periods of great activity interspersed with periods of virtual abandonment. The copper district is currently idle because of high operating costs.

North from Altaville there is little of geologic interest along the highway until Calaveritas Creek is reached. The gently rolling grazing land is probably much like the ancestral Eocene land surface. Remnants of auriferous gravels can be seen to the east of the road particularly between Calaveritas Creek and San Andreas. The bedrock is schist and greenstone of the Calaveras formation. In several places along Calaveritas Creek, both southeast and southwest of San Andreas, limestone lenses occur in the Calaveras which are suitable for use in making Portland cement. Although parts of the lenses are dolomitic and carry too high a magnesia content for cement, excellent bodies of cement-grade limestone occur in them and are being exploited at the present time. The Calaveras Cement Company has a large plant situated a short distance west of Highway 49, 2½ miles south of San Andreas. The company allows visitors at its plant which is well worth going through. Historic Kentucky House

FIG. 25. Aerial view of part of the Calaveras Cement Company plant southwest of San Andreas. *Photo by courtesy of L. A. Parsons, Calaveras Cement Co.*

FIG. 26.   Quarrying operation in one of the limestone pits of the Calaveras Cement Company near San Andreas.
Photo by courtesy of L. A. Parsons, Calaveras Cement Co.

is located near by. The plant can be reached by two different roads connecting with Highway 49 close to San Andreas. A private road and overpass which connects the plant to its eastern limestone quarries crosses Highway 49 at the Calaveritas Creek bridge.

San Andreas, as the name implies, was first settled by Spanish Californian miners prior to the advent of the Yankee. As usual they were persecuted and driven out of town whereas other minority groups such as the Chinese were allowed to remain. Present day San Andreas is an attractive town, more or less typical of the Mother Lode, and full of old buildings dating from as early as 1851. Division of Highways Historical Marker 222 stands at the corner of Highways 49 and 12. Highway 12 connects with the old towns of Railroad Flat and Westpoint to the northeast of San Andreas. As county seat of Calaveras County, San Andreas boasts both the County Courthouse and County Museum. The museum occupies one of the best preserved, oldest buildings in town and contains rocks, minerals, artifacts, Indian handcraft, and miscellaneous objects and manuscripts of historical interest.

Proceeding northward from San Andreas, Highway 49 traverses four miles of rolling grazing land of no particular geologic interest. The headframe and buildings of the Kate Hageman mine are located near the bridge which crosses the North Fork of the Calaveras River, 2.2 miles northwest of San Andreas. The Kate Hageman was developed during the 1930's and considerable modern mill equipment was installed. Both opencut and underground mining has been attempted there. The mine has been idle for some time. Wall rocks are greenstone and slate; a serpentine contact is close by to the west. The creek bottoms near the Kate Hageman have been worked for placer gold.

Two miles northwest of the Kate Hageman mine, a rather extensive group of Tertiary deposits is exposed on both sides of the highway from the vicinity of Chili Gulch to Mokelumne Hill. The ancient Mokelumne Hill river channel once traversed this region in a southwesterly direction and was joined, in the Chili Gulch vicinity, by a tributary which entered from the direction of San Andreas. Remnants of the old channel gravels have been extensively worked for gold by hydraulic and other placer means. The lofty faces of the hydraulic pits are not visible from Highway 49 but some of the gravels are exposed in road cuts east of Chili Gulch. The gravels lie nonconformably on schists and greenstones of the Calaveras formation and are overlain by the rhyolite tuff of the Valley Springs formation and the andesite and andesite gravels of the Mehrten formation in that order. Unconformities exist between the Valley Springs and Mehrten and even within the Mehrten itself. The Valley Springs is probably Miocene and the Mehrten is probably Pliocene at least in part. Cliffed outcrops of yellowish-gray tuff of the Valley Springs formation are prominent in many places along the Mokelumne grade. Exposures of the Mehrten can best be seen a short distance west of the town of

Mokelumne Hill along Highway 8. A quarter of a mile south of the Calaveras Crystal mine, the Calaveras bedrock has been intruded by diorite. Dioritic rocks form the basement on which the Tertiary rests over a large area in the vicinity of Mokelumne Hill.

The Calaveras Crystal is a drift mine driven beneath the Valley Springs rhyolite opposite the Chile Creek placer diggings. It can be reached via dirt road from Highway 49, the road joining Highway 49 from the east at a point 6.5 miles from San Andreas or 2.5 miles from Mokelumne Hill. The mine is on a branch of the Mokelumne Hill channel system known as the Tunnel Hill channel. The large quartz crystals which have made the mine famous are partly of optical and electronic grade. Considerable quartz for this purpose was marketed during the recent war emergency. Crystals weighing as much as 100 pounds each have been taken from the Calaveras Crystal. An adjoining mine on the McSorley Ranch operated by the Rough Diamond Mining Company also produced considerable quantities of optical-grade quartz. Although not so well known as the Calaveras Crystal, reserves of quartz crystals in this mine appear to be greater than those of its more famous neighbor.

Mokelumne Hill was founded in 1848 by ex-members of Stevensons Regiment of Mexican war fame. A stone historical monument erected by the Native Daughters of the Golden West is located close to the three story I.O.O.F. building. The latter building was erected in 1854 and added to in 1861 and is the first three story building in the Mother Lode country. Mokelumne Hill and Jackson once engaged in a feud over the problem of which town should get the honor of being county seat. Originally, Double Springs, some miles to the west of Mokelumne Hill, had acted as county seat until rapidly growing Mokelumne Hill claimed the honor. Jackson finally "seceded" from Calaveras County and formed a county and county seat all its own, now Amador County. The present Amador-Calaveras County line follows the course of the Mokelumne River in this area. San Andreas is now the county seat of Calaveras County. Highways 5 and 8 cross 49 at Mokelumne Hill, Highway 8 continuing on to the east to mining districts in the vicinity of Westpoint.

Near the junction of Highways 8 and 49, a group of underground rooms and quarries, from which rhyolite tuff building stone was taken, can be observed. Mokelumne Hill was fortunate in having so satisfactory a source of building material so close at hand.

Roadcuts to the west of Mokelumne Hill along Highway 8 afforded closeup views of the late Tertiary volcanic sequence. Three miles from the junction of 8 and 49, a long cut exposes the trace of a low-angle thrust fault which cuts both the schist bedrock and the overlying Mehrten rocks. This is an unusual type of post-Pliocene faulting for this area, although the fault is probably not of major extent. The trace of this same fault can be seen in the undercut face of one of the volcanic plugs to be seen on the south side of the road three-tenths of a mile farther west. This group of plugs, of which there are three besides the Golden Gate plug considerably farther west, are made up of a rock described as hornblende andesite. These supposedly are the vents from which the Mehrten volcanics were derived.

MOKELUMNE HILL TO PLYMOUTH—MAP 5

Between Mokelumne Hill and the canyon of the Mokelumne River the terrain is hilly. The Tertiary gravel and volcanic series has largely been stripped off and the tributaries of the Mokelumne have badly dissected the old Eocene surface. West from town, Jackson Butte, a lofty volcanic plug, stands out above the other hills. Far beyond and to the northwest the metal water tank of the Argonaut mine can be seen on the ridge top. The bedrock along the highway is diorite and related plutonics until well beyond the Mokelumne River. A few gravel remnants outcrop near the road within sight of Mokelumne Hill.

One and four-tenths miles north of the Mokelumne River bridge the road passes through a thick series of tuffaceous gravels which are part of the placer ground of the Butte City mining district. The site of Butte City can be located by the ruins of the Butte Store and State Division of Highways Historical Marker 39. Beyond Butte City 1.3 miles, an oiled road turns to the west which connects with the old placer camp of Middle Bar on the Mokelumne River about four miles from Butte City. The bridge which now crosses the Mokelumne is about at the old site. The river bottom is now flooded most of the year by the waters backed up behind Pardee Dam. Little Bar is commemorated by State Division of Highways Historical Marker 36. A mile farther north, a road from Clinton leads off to the east. The Clinton mining district is on the East Belt close to the granodiorite contact. The Clinton Consolidated and Clinton Bar are the best known lode mines of the district. Clinton was a placer district before the lode mines were developed. State Division of Highways Historical Marker 37 marks the turnoff to Clinton.

The dumps and mine buildings of the Zeila mine are located close to Highway 49, six-tenths of a mile south of Jackson. The Zeila was first opened in the 1860's, was closed down during the latter half of the 70's and was a heavy producer from 1880 to 1914. The mine has an inclined shaft which is 1700 feet deep along an incline of 65° average dip. The ore occurs in quartz stringers in a gouge composed of decomposed rocks of several types. The veins lie on the contact of Calaveras slate and schist and greenstones of uncertain age. One drift is over 3000 feet long. Total production of the Zeila has been more than $5,000,000.

Northward from the Zeila mine to the vicinity of Plymouth, a distance of about 12 miles, the Mother Lode has produced gold far in excess of $160,000,000. This is by far the richest yield recorded along the Mother Lode for any sector of equal length, and is exceeded in California, in total gold produced, only by the Grass Valley district of Nevada County.

The geology of this highly productive strip is complicated both in structure and in lithologic similarities, and there are many diverse interpretations of the geology by those currently at work there. Most of the productive mines are on a branch of the Mother Lode thrust fault system known locally as the Gold Thrust. The main Mother Lode fault which lies about a mile to the east of the Gold Thrust is nonproductive along this sector. The strike of these two faults is roughly N. 30° W. and parallels the regional trend of the structure for the most part. Other faults of similar type and trend occur several miles to the west of Jackson and are undoubtedly other branches of the Mother Lode system. The Jurassic sediments and metavolcanics in this area are badly deformed into a series of tight, overturned, isoclinal folds which have been further complicated by the several thrust faults mentioned above.

Jackson, the county seat of Amador County, is a vigorous, modern town combining the old with the new. Many of its old buildings have had their faces lifted so that one would hardly recognize their true vintage. Jackson bears the name of Colonel Alden Jackson who has also been honored by having the Tuolumne County town of Jacksonville named for him. The town dates from at least 1849 and probably before. Botilleas, the original name for the site, indicates that, like many other gold camps, Spanish Californians were the original settlers. Jackson is very proud of its one-time Congressman, benefactor, and native son, Anthony Caminetti, who did a great deal for Jackson and for Amador County in general. A monument to his memory has been erected beside Highway 49 immediately north of the business district.

Jackson Gate is a small town located 1.5 miles north of Jackson and reached via paved road from either Jackson or Martell. Although small, Jackson Gate is picturesque and is the possessor of a group of very interesting relics of the past mining ventures. To the north and east of town are several huge wheels which were built in 1902 to raise tailings, or mill waste, from the ground level of the Kennedy mine, situated a half mile to the west, to the summit of a ridge beyond which lay the tailings disposal dump. Although partly dismantled, the wheels were once equipped with a circle of 176 buckets, a belt drive, and an electric motor each. They were 68 feet in diameter and raised the tailings a vertical distance of 48 feet each. The tailings elevators connected gravity flumes in which the tailings flowed from mill to dump. Sheet metal buildings once housed each wheel but these have been removed.

Two of the greatest mines on the Mother Lode are located slightly more than a mile northwest of Jackson. These were exceedingly large operations both above and below ground and are famous landmarks along Highway 49. The Kennedy, with its lofty headframe and huge sheet-iron-enclosed mill, lies a short distance to the east of Highway 49. The original Kennedy claim was located in 1856 and has since been consolidated with several others. It was a minor working until 1871

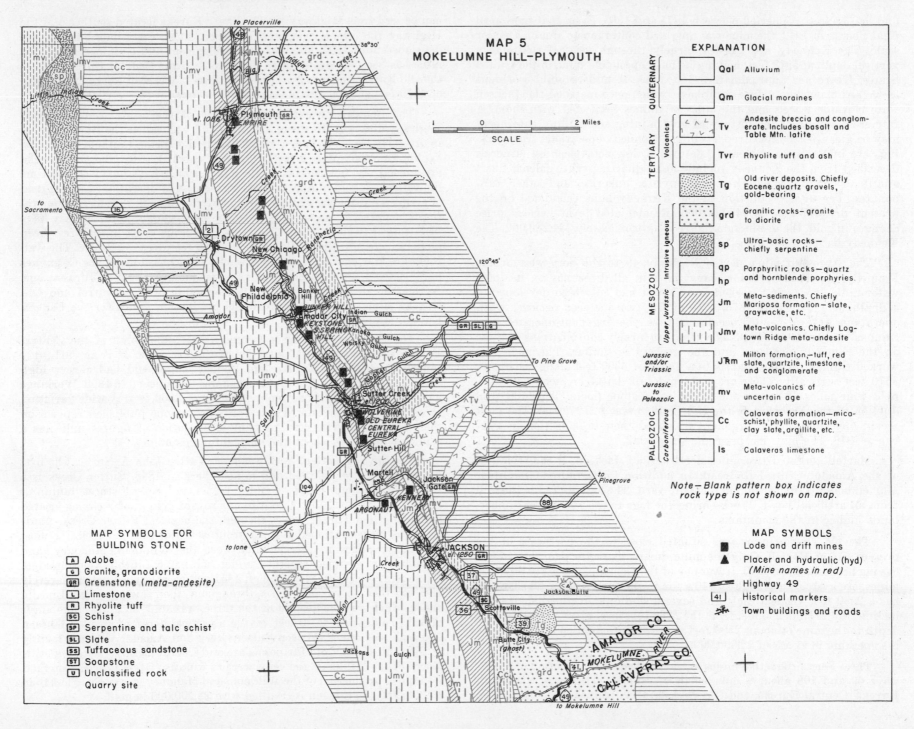

MAP 5
MOKELUMNE HILL-PLYMOUTH

SCALE

1 0 1 2 Miles

EXPLANATION

QUATERNARY
Qal Alluvium
Qm Glacial moraines

TERTIARY — Volcanics
Tv Andesite breccia and conglomerate. Includes basalt and Table Mtn. latite
Tvr Rhyolite tuff and ash
Tg Old river deposits. Chiefly Eocene quartz gravels, gold-bearing

MESOZOIC — Intrusive igneous
grd Granitic rocks—granite to diorite
sp Ultra-basic rocks— chiefly serpentine
qp hp Porphyritic rocks—quartz and hornblende porphyries.

Upper Jurassic
Jm Meta-sediments. Chiefly Mariposa formation—slate, graywacke, etc.
Jmv Meta-volcanics. Chiefly Logtown Ridge meta-andesite

Jurassic and/or Triassic
Jℝm Milton formation—tuff, red slate, quartzite, limestone, and conglomerate

Jurassic to Paleozoic
mv Meta-volcanics of uncertain age

PALEOZOIC — Carboniferous
Cc Calaveras formation—mica-schist, phyllite, quartzite, clay slate, argillite, etc.
ls Calaveras limestone

Note—Blank pattern box indicates rock type is not shown on map.

MAP SYMBOLS FOR BUILDING STONE
Ⓐ Adobe
Ⓖ Granite, granodiorite
ⒼⓇ Greenstone (meta-andesite)
Ⓛ Limestone
Ⓡ Rhyolite tuff
Ⓢⓒ Schist
Ⓢⓟ Serpentine and talc schist
Ⓢⓛ Slate
Ⓢⓢ Tuffaceous sandstone
Ⓢⓣ Soapstone
Ⓤ Unclassified rock
Quarry site

MAP SYMBOLS
◼ Lode and drift mines
▲ Placer and hydraulic (hyd) (Mine names in red)
══ Highway 49
[41] Historical markers
✳ Town buildings and roads

and had an inactive period between 1875 and 1885. From that time until final closing in 1942, the mine was operated continuously and on a major scale. The Kennedy was worked largely through vertical shafts to a vertical depth of 5912 feet, making it the deepest gold mine in the United States. There are approximately 150 miles of underground workings as well as extensive surface equipment which once included the Jackson Gate elevator wheels and the miles of flumes connected with them. A fair cross section of the history of gold mining and milling equipment may be gleaned from past reports of the Kennedy operations. The workings are in Mariposa slate and Logtown Ridge metavolcanics. Minerals described from the Kennedy include gold, quartz, pyrite, galena, fluorapatite, strengite, sphalerite, chalcopyrite, ankerite, and other carbonates. The total production of the Kennedy mine calculated on the present price of gold is $45,000,000. Recalculated to fit various price changes in gold, the production figure is approximately $34,280,000. The Kennedy has been idle since 1942.

The Argonaut mine, across Highway 49 to the northwest of the Kennedy, can be located for many miles in all directions by its lofty water tank. It was first worked in 1850 but had only been developed to a depth of 150 feet by 1876. Except for two one-year periods, when operations were suspended because of fires, the Argonaut operated continuously from 1893 to 1942. The veins are largely continuations of those on the Kennedy property and the geology is similar. The mine was worked through inclined shafts to a depth of 6300 feet along the dip or 5570 feet vertically. There are eight miles of drifts, crosscuts and tunnels, four miles of raises, and 50 miles of stope floors. The total production of the Argonaut to the end of 1943 was $25,179,160. The most recent operators of the Argonaut dissolved their organization in February 1948. The mine has been idle since 1943.

Martell, situated two miles northwest of Jackson, is the terminus of the Amador Central Railroad. In addition to its railroad facilities, Martell boasts a lumber mill and curing yard. The logs are fed to the mill from an artificial pond. Trucks bring the logs to the pond from timberlands higher in the mountains.

The old Oneida mine was situated close to the northeast of the present site of Martell. Only the mine dumps mark the site, the Oneida having been idle since 1913. It was one of the richest of the early-day lode mines, ore averaging as high as $40 a ton in the early 1860's. The Oneida has a 2280 foot vertical shaft and several shallower inclined shafts. An inclined winze sunk 250 feet from the 2280 foot level gives a total vertical depth to the mine of about 2500 feet. The total production of the Oneida is something in excess of $2,500,000.

Three very productive mines are located near the junction of Highways 49 and 108 about a mile north of Martell. These are the South Eureka, Central Eureka, and Old Eureka. Headframes of the latter two can be seen from Highway 49. The South Eureka located southeast of the Highway 108 intersection, was discovered at an early date but was not developed until 1891. Much of the development and maintenance of this mine has been integrated with operations in the Central Eureka as has the Old Eureka, since 1924. The South Eureka has been worked to a depth of 4100 feet and has produced gold to the amount of $5,300,000.

The Central Eureka, located north of the South Eureka across Highway 108, was discovered in 1855 and was called the Summit mine in its early days. It had a small production prior to 1865 but major exploitation took place after 1896. The Central Eureka and Old Eureka are among the few Mother Lode mines which have survived wartime limitations on gold mining and the rising cost of operation. A great deal of credit is due the present management for being able to remain in operation when other large workings such as the Argonaut and Kennedy have been forced to close down. The Central Eureka shaft is 4965 feet deep along an average dip of 70° or about 4650 feet deep vertically. The wall rocks are Mariposa slate and graywacke and greenstone of the Cosumnes and Logtown Ridge members of the Amador group, all of Jurassic age. Authorities disagree on the early production of the Central and Old Eureka mines, but the best available production figure for the Central Eureka is $17,000,000.

The Old Eureka mine is located a half mile north of the Central Eureka headframe in the outskirts of Sutter Creek. It is an early day consolidation of the Eureka and Badger claims and had a very high early-day production. The Old Eureka was first opened in 1852. Workings have been developed to an inclined depth of 3500 feet. A wide variation in early-day production figures exists in various published reports on the Old Eureka. The most probable compilation of figures indicates a total production of about $17,400,000 for this mine.

The town of Sutter Creek was named after John A. Sutter who first visited the region in 1846 and mined there in 1848. Sutter Creek is a rather harmonious blend of older frame and recent stucco buildings nestled among low hills. A continuous row of gold quartz claims located along the Gold Thrust passes through the heart of Sutter Creek. Aside from the aforementioned Eureka group south of Sutter Creek, the most productive mines in this vicinity were the Wildman, Mahoney, and Lincoln now grouped together under the name Lincoln Consolidated. These mines were discovered about 1851 and were worked both separately and together at various times throughout their history. The Lincoln shaft, which was the deepest of the three, was sunk on an average angle of 63° to a depth of 2000 feet, giving a vertical depth of about 1760 feet. Ore bodies of mines between Sutter Creek and Amador City are mainly at the fault contact of Mariposa slate and Logtown Ridge meta-andesite. North of the Wildman, the veins were as wide as 45 feet near the surface. Combined production of the Wildman and Mahoney was slightly less than $5,000,000; the Lincoln is credited with $2,200,000 in gold.

An interesting side trip to the old placer and hydraulic mining center of Volcano can be made via good paved road east from Sutter Creek. The Volcano placers were discovered early in the 1850's and the town soon boasted a population of over 5000. The drive up Sutter Creek canyon is scenic and the town of Volcano, although partly in ruins, retains much of its early-day color. In common with Murphys and Columbia, Volcano has not been modernized. There are several limestone caves in the vicinity.

Amador City, 2.2 miles northwest of Sutter Creek, is the locus of another group of rich mines. The Amador Creek placers were located in 1848 but were never very rich, and it was not until the first lode gold strike in 1851 that Amador City begin to grow. Amador City has much the same setting and background as Sutter Creek which it resembles in many ways. Strangely enough, a Baptist minister made the initial discovery in Amador County, which was first known as the Minister's claim. Later it was developed into the Original Amador mine.

The Original Amador, now a consolidation of six claims is a very complex working comprising over nine miles of drifts, crosscuts, and raises. These open off from a 1238-foot inclined shaft. Estimated total production for this mine is $3,500,000. The Original Amador is located about a fourth of a mile northeast of town.

Best known and most productive of the Amador City mines is the Keystone, located southeast of town. It dates from 1853, being a consolidation of several pre-existing claims. Ore from these had been milled in arrastres from 1861 to 1863. The main shaft is 2680 feet deep along an average incline of 52°. Much of the ore taken from this mine was of sulfarsenide or sulfantimonide type which is somewhat unusual among Mother Lode ores. The total production of the Keystone is about $24,-500,000.

Immediately to the east of the Keystone is the South Spring Hill mine, located in 1851. The South Spring Hill shaft is 1200 feet deep along a 60° incline. Before passing into the hands of the Keystone interests in 1920, the mine had been credited with a production of $1,092,472.

Highway 49 turns west at Amador City and follows along Amador Creek for over a mile before turning north toward Drytown. The road cuts are all in meta-andesite of the Logtown Ridge formation. A thick section of this formation is exposed along this sector of the highway.

Drytown was founded in the spring of 1848 when rich placer ground was discovered there. Its heydey was prior to 1857 before the placer diggings became exhausted. Drytown claims the distinction of being the discovery point of the first placer gold taken from Amador County. Division of Highways Historical Marker 21 is located near the junction of Highway 49 and the Drytown-New Chicago-Amador City road. The latter is paved and is an alternate route from Amador City to Drytown.

Along this road are the old mining camps of New Chicago and New Philadelphia and the productive Gover, Bunker Hill, Fremont, Italian, and Treasure mines. The former two are credited with producing over $5,000,000 each. Such picturesque names as Lower Rancheria, Bloody Gulch, Rattlesnake Gulch, and Murderer's Gulch are connected with placering in this vicinity.

Highway 49 merges with Highway 16, 1.2 miles northwest of Drytown and bends sharply to the east for half a mile before continuing northward into Plymouth. The history of Plymouth is connected with the ups and downs of the lode mines nearby, which same were discovered in 1852. The Plymouth Consolidated mine is the most famous one in this vicinity. Like most other large Mother Lode mines, the Plymouth Consolidated is a merger of many old claims. At least 16 claims or parts thereof were consolidated into the one property. Most of the ore is reported to have come from the Simpson, Aden, and Oaks claims. The deepest part of the mine is at least 4450 feet deep along a shaft which is partly vertical and partly inclined. Although the veins are on a continuation of the same Gold Thrust on which the Amador City and Sutter Creek mines are located, the wall rocks in the Plymouth Consolidated are confined to Mariposa slate. The total production of the mine has been estimated at more than $13,500,000. The Plymouth Consolidated is the most northerly of the major mines of the Mother Lode. Above Plymouth, the veins contain much more limited ore shoots and finally fray out into stringer lodes or veinlet stockworks. The workings in Georgetown, Garden Valley, Greenwood, and Spanish Diggings are of this type.

The old placer mining camp of Fiddletown can be reached by a paved road leading east from Plymouth. Fiddletown was settled by Missourians in 1849. The somewhat picturesque name was changed to Oleta in 1878 and still appears as such on most maps.

PLYMOUTH TO PLACERVILLE—MAP 6

Northbound from Plymouth, Highway 49 changes its northwesterly trend and goes almost due north for 12 miles. Over much of this distance the road lies in a narrow valley close to the watercourses of Big Indian Creek and the North Fork of the Cosumnes River. A mile above the old mining camp of Nashville, the highway crosses Logtown Ridge and drops into Logtown Ravine. The latter opens out onto low rolling meadowland in the vicinity of El Dorado. The land surface from Logtown Ravine on to Placerville has been resurrected by Quaternary erosion and the present topography is much as it was in late Cretaceous or early Eocene time. Bright red deeply weathered areas of the bedrock series and remnants of Tertiary gravels are evidence of the transformation.

The Amador Star and Bay State mines are in the vicinity of the Enterprise schoolhouse, four miles north of Plymouth. These are located on the west side of the highway and close to it. They are 40 years younger than the mines below Amador City and are much less extensive. Production has been intermittent and unspectacular.

A mile farther north, Highway 49 crosses the Cosumnes River and Amador-El Dorado County line. The Cosumnes branches into two forks just above this spot, the South Fork cutting immediately across the ridge to the east and the North Fork flowing north for several miles parallel to the highway. West of the Cosumnes River bridge, also known as Huse Bridge, the river flows in a deep canyon cut through Logtown Ridge. A hike of a few miles down this canyon is well worth the geologist's time. Along the stream bed are exposed type sections of two members of the Amador group, the Logtown Ridge meta-andesite agglomerate and the Cosumnes meta-sediments composed of conglomeratic, sandy, and tuffaceous beds.

Two miles north of the Cosumnes River bridge is the old mining camp of Nashville or Quartzburg. The site of Nashville was originally an old Indian camping spot or rancheria, and the mining camp was one of the first lode camps in the state. The Tennessee-Nashville mine, also known as the Havilah, claims to have operated the first stamp mill in California, and ore from the mine was crushed in arrastres previous to that time. The Tennessee-Nashville was the first lode mine in El Dorado County and one of the first in the state. The stamp mill was manufactured in Cincinnati and brought around the Horn. Known production for the Tennessee-Nashville is in excess of $231,000 but there are no records for several periods of activity. The mine is about 1000 feet deep.

North of the Tennessee-Nashville a distance of 1.3 miles are the dumps of the Montezuma mine. The Montezuma had considerable elaborate equipment at the site in the 1930's but this has since been removed. The Montezuma has a history similar to that of the Tennessee-Nashville with which much of the development work has been connected. Immediately north of the Montezuma mine the old and historic Kings Store road leads off to the northeast. This road connects with the Red Bird, Union, Martinez, and Crusader mines which are along Martinez Creek. The Union is credited with being the largest producer in El Dorado County. Incomplete production figures indicate a yield in excess of $2,700,000.

Two mines, the Pocahontas and the Ophir, are located in Logtown Ravine close to Highway 49 between two and three miles southwest of El Dorado. They are of interest to geologists because the veins are on the contact of Logtown Ridge meta-andesite and a quartz porphyry and may not be related to the Mother Lode. The quartz porphyry is closely associated with granodiorite in this locality and is either derived from it or intimately intruded by it. The Pocahontas is more than 1000 feet deep along a rather shallow dip of about 45°.

Two miles south of El Dorado several ruins of old stone buildings can be seen on either side of the highway. The best preserved of these is a partly dugout structure half of which is below ground level. A substantial part of the walls are made from granodiorite arrastre stones. Arrastres were used extensively in connection with the mines between Plymouth and Placerville and their partly shaped stones made good building blocks. The arrastre method of grinding ore was borrowed from the Spanish Californians but it is probable that those in the El Dorado district were "Yankee" made.

El Dorado, originally known as Mud Springs, was a camp on the Carson Emigrant Trail long before gold rush days. The name was changed during the height of the gold rush at the time of the incorporation of the town. Although attractively situated in the midst of a lumbering, cattle grazing, and gold mining region, El Dorado has never gained the impetus toward growth enjoyed by its near-neighbor Placerville. A sawmill and lime plant are located close to town and many early day buildings, both well preserved and in ruins, can be seen there.

Diamond Springs is located near one of the richest of the early day placer diggings in the vicinity of Placerville. Like El Dorado, it was an emigrant camp before gold rush days. Both Diamond Springs and El Dorado are to one side of the Highway 50 cross-country route but are served by railroads and are active lumbering towns.

Placerville was founded in 1848 either by James Marshall or a Cosumnes River rancher named William Daylor. Both were there at different times in the spring of '48. Placerville was known variously as Old Dry Diggin's and Hangtown, but was incorporated as Placerville in 1854. Placerville is probably the largest and most up-to-date town on the Mother Lode, with vast lumber, railroad, and tourist interests. It is served by Highways 49 and 50 and by the Southern Pacific Railroad. The place is filled with old buildings and other spots of historical interest which have been adroitly preserved among the modern structures of the town. Many of the old buildings have been rehabilitated and house many types of business enterprise. Placerville is also justly proud of its new structures such as the County Courthouse building. Few places in California are as steeped in early-day history as Placerville. Old placer and hydraulic diggings surround the town on all sides and appear within its limits; fine old churches abound; and the pine-covered hills to the east of town form a fitting backdrop. J. M. Studebaker, who later founded an automobile empire, learned his trade in the blacksmith shops of Placerville. Although the gold of the vicinity has been largely dissipated, the timber and water resources remain and the county still flourishes.

In addition to the placer diggings, several lode mines were developed near Placerville. The most successful of these is the Pacific Quartz mine situated on a hill on the south side of town. It is about 2000 feet deep via vertical and inclined shafts and winzes. The ore is gold-bearing arsenopyrite containing considerable silver. Some ore bodies are in talc schist. The wall rocks are Mariposa slate. There are intrusive bodies of serpen-

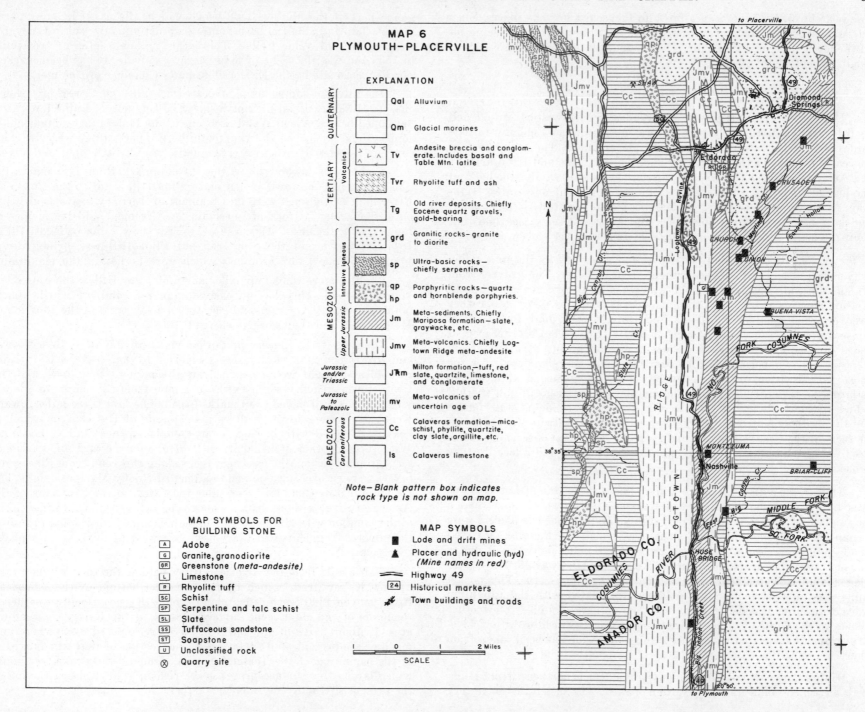

MAP 6
PLYMOUTH—PLACERVILLE

EXPLANATION

QUATERNARY	Qal	Alluvium
	Qm	Glacial moraines
TERTIARY — Volcanics	Tv	Andesite breccia and conglomerate. Includes basalt and Table Mtn. latite
	Tvr	Rhyolite tuff and ash
	Tg	Old river deposits. Chiefly Eocene quartz gravels, gold-bearing
MESOZOIC — Intrusive igneous	grd	Granitic rocks—granite to diorite
	sp	Ultra-basic rocks—chiefly serpentine
	qp hp	Porphyritic rocks—quartz and hornblende porphyries.
Upper Jurassic	Jm	Meta-sediments. Chiefly Mariposa formation—slate, graywacke, etc.
	Jmv	Meta-volcanics. Chiefly Logtown Ridge meta-andesite
Jurassic and/or Triassic	JȚ̵m	Milton formation,—tuff, red slate, quartzite, limestone, and conglomerate
Jurassic to Paleozoic	mv	Meta-volcanics of uncertain age
PALEOZOIC — Carboniferous	Cc	Calaveras formation—mica-schist, phyllite, quartzite, clay slate, argillite, etc.
	ls	Calaveras limestone

Note—Blank pattern box indicates rock type is not shown on map.

MAP SYMBOLS FOR
BUILDING STONE

- [A] Adobe
- [G] Granite, granodiorite
- [GR] Greenstone (meta-andesite)
- [L] Limestone
- [R] Rhyolite tuff
- [SC] Schist
- [SP] Serpentine and talc schist
- [SL] Slate
- [SS] Tuffaceous sandstone
- [ST] Soapstone
- [U] Unclassified rock
- [⊗] Quarry site

MAP SYMBOLS

- ■ Lode and drift mines
- ▲ Placer and hydraulic (hyd)
  (Mine names in red)
- ‖ Highway 49
- [24] Historical markers
- Town buildings and roads

SCALE

1   0   1   2 Miles

tine near by which have been altered to talc-schist in some places. Such talc and serpentine rocks are exposed near the Safeway Store parking lot on the main street of Placerville. The Pacific Quartz mine has a recorded production of $1,486,000.

PLACERVILLE TO AUBURN—MAP 7

From Placerville, Highway 49 resumes a northwesterly trend and soon leaves the Mother Lode to traverse an area almost lacking in lode mines and having but widely scattered placer camps. The relief steadily increases because of the proximity of the many forks and tributaries of the American River. The steeper canyon slopes are heavily wooded and the logged-off areas are covered with brush. For about four miles, Highway 49 traverses a bedrock of Mariposa slate, Logtown Ridge meta-andesite, intrusive quartz porphyry, and Calaveras schist; beyond that limit the bedrock is granodiorite for a distance of over eleven miles.

Coloma, site of Marshall's discovery of gold in 1848, lies in a valley traversed by the South Fork of the American River. The gravels from which Marshall washed the gold which made history are not the old Eocene deposits from which so much placer gold was taken, but rather are reworked Quaternary sands and gravels. The gold found along present day Sierran rivers is derived partly from recent erosion of gold lodes but more generally from recent erosion of pre-existing stream deposits. The timberlands which first interested Marshall have, for the most part, been cut off, the gravels were soon exhausted and Coloma is largely a town of memories. The vicinity of Sutters Mill and the hill which overlooks it to the southwest have been set aside as state parks. On the south side of town the home of the poet J. Edwin Markham can be seen on the west side of the main street. Centennial observances have resulted in the erection of many suitable monuments and a local-history museum.

Downriver a distance of 1.5 miles is the placer camp of Lotus. Lotus was first known as Marshall and then as Uniontown. It once had a population of 2000, but this dwindled to a handful once the placers were exhausted. Two fine old brick structures remain on the site. A paved road connecting Lotus with Shingle Springs and Highway 50 passes through town and at its northern outskirts joins Highway 49. The Stuckslager mine is located near this road one mile south of Lotus. This pocket mine was unusual in that the gold was associated with the vanadium mica roscoelite. Roscoelite is a very rare mineral found in few other places in the United States. It occurred in fine greenish-brown or clove-brown scales associated with quartz and gold. None has been taken from there for some time.

Half a mile north of Lotus, a paved road turns northeast from Highway 49 which connects with Garden Valley. The latter lies in a very scenic part of the Mother Lode which will be discussed in later paragraphs. Two and a half miles beyond this junction is the ruin of Meyer's Dance Hall and Wine Cellar. This local "miners' delight" was built in 1855 and was the scene of many a gay escapade. It has been marked as a historical site by the El Dorado County Chamber of Commerce.

The Lilyama copper mine is located 5.4 miles northwest of Coloma close to Highway 49 on the north side. The Lilyama is a minor working developed before World War I. It is one of the few contact-metamorphic copper deposits in the Sierran foothills. Copper values were in chalcopyrite associated with pyrite, magnetite, and a little gold and silver.

Eight miles beyond Lotus the old landmark Pilot Hill marks the placer diggings and town of that name. Pilot Hill is not on the American River and its diggings were in a remnant of Tertiary gravel which lies on a greenstone bedrock of uncertain age. Frémont and his men were reputed to be the first "Americanos" to visit the vicinity of Pilot Hill in 1844. Mining began there in 1849 but Pilot Hill was principally a jumping-off place for the mines which were higher in the mountains.

Slightly more than four miles north of Pilot Hill is the crossroads known as Cool. This was an early-day placer camp of which almost nothing remains. A garage and gas station are located at the junction of Highway 49 and the Georgetown road.

The route from Placerville to Cool via Garden Valley, Georgetown, and Greenwood is in most respects superior to that traversed by Highway 49 and might well be named an alternate to that highway. The Georgetown turnoff is eight-tenths of a mile from the center of Placerville and is a well paved, well marked road. The first three miles toward Kelsey and Georgetown lie down a steep side of Big Canyon which is heavily timbered with incense cedar, Douglas spruce, and yellow pine. With the exception of a narrow belt of greenstone and an occasional serpentine intrusion, the basement rocks along this road from Placerville to Georgetown are Jurassic meta-sediments, chiefly Mariposa slate. The Pacific Minerals Company slate mine is located on the east bank of the American River a short distance above the bridge. It is 2.3 miles north of the junction with Highway 49. The slate is mined for roofing granules, the mineral fragments which are used as a wearing surface on asphalt-felt roofing.

Half a mile from the American River bridge, the road winds up the narrow Kelsey grade which climbs from the bottom of the American River canyon 1100 feet to the upland around Kelsey. Deeply weathered remnants of the old Eocene surface abound in the Kelsey-Georgetown area. Brilliant red soil and lateritic clays are exposed everywhere and much of the present land surface is a resurrection of that which existed at the beginning of the Tertiary period. Some of the gravel remnants which lay on this surface proved to be rich in gold. Kelseys Ravine at the present site of Kelsey was one of these.

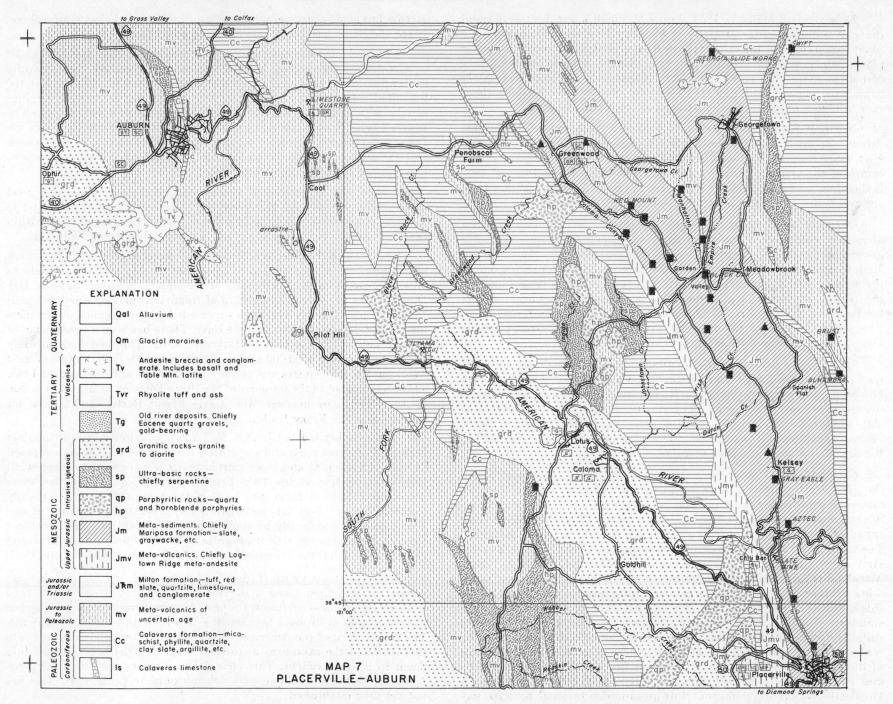

EXPLANATION

QUATERNARY

Qal — Alluvium

Qm — Glacial moraines

TERTIARY

Volcanics

Tv — Andesite breccia and conglomerate. Includes basalt and Table Mtn. latite

Tvr — Rhyolite tuff and ash

Tg — Old river deposits. Chiefly Eocene quartz gravels, gold-bearing

MESOZOIC

Intrusive igneous

grd — Granitic rocks—granite to diorite

sp — Ultra-basic rocks—chiefly serpentine

qp — Porphyritic rocks—quartz and hornblende porphyries.

hp — (hornblende porphyries)

Upper Jurassic

Jm — Meta-sediments. Chiefly Mariposa formation—slate, graywacke, etc.

Jmv — Meta-volcanics. Chiefly Logtown Ridge meta-andesite

Jurassic and/or Triassic

JTrm — Milton formation,—tuff, red slate, quartzite, limestone, and conglomerate

Jurassic to Paleozoic

mv — Meta-volcanics of uncertain age

PALEOZOIC

Carboniferous

Cc — Calaveras formation—mica-schist, phyllite, quartzite, clay slate, argillite, etc.

ls — Calaveras limestone

MAP 7
PLACERVILLE—AUBURN

Kelsey was founded in 1851. James Marshall's last days were spent there. A building on the property of his Gray Eagle mine once housed a pioneer museum but the exhibits have been moved to Columbia and other places. Only a huge arrastre-stone remains of the old exhibits once displayed there. The adit of the Gray Eagle lode mine is immediately behind the museum building. It never paid, and Marshall died without ever having a hand in a really successful mining venture.

North of Kelsey, a distance of 1.4 miles, a road leads off to the east through Spanish Flat and Meadowbrook, ending at Georgetown. Spanish Flat, more recently known as Louisville, was one of a great many placer camps of the vicinity dating from about 1850. The Alhambra and Lost Lode mines are located close to the Louisville road. They are shallow open cut and tunnel workings in stringer lodes. Both are idle.

Garden Valley, originally named Johntown, is 5.5 miles northwest of Kelsey. Johntown was a placer camp which later became a vegetable growing center, hence the present name. The entire area in which Garden Valley, Spanish Flat, Georgetown, and Greenwood are located is one of the most beautiful landscapes in California and is bound to find increasing favor as a recreational region. The broad rolling meadowlands are bordered by flowing streams and beautiful stands of coniferous trees. The primitive area of the Rubicon River northeast of Georgetown is almost untouched by the inroads of man.

Half a mile beyond Garden Valley, a road to Meadowbrook leads past the Black Oak mine near the Garden Valley school. The Black Oak has been one of the best mines in El Dorado County, having produced over a million dollars in gold. The veins are on the contact of Mariposa slate and greenstone and are the same series as in the Alpine and Beebe mines to the north in Georgetown. The workings are rather shallow but the drifts and crosscuts are extensive.

Georgetown, 7.3 miles from Garden Valley, looks much as it did in the '50's. Mining activity there was initiated in 1849 by a party of placer miners from Oregon, and the site was first known as Growlersburg. Several lode mines helped keep the town active after the placers were exhausted. Lumbering and fruit-growing are now the principal activities. The main street has many well preserved buildings such as the Masonic Hall erected in 1852 and the Balsar House dating from 1859. Edwin Markham taught school in Georgetown in the 1880's. Like those of many other Mother Lode towns, Georgetown's pioneers rallied to the Union side during the Civil War. An armory was built in 1862 which is still standing. The El Dorado County Chamber of Commerce has erected suitable historical markers at sites of special interest. The Alpine at the center of town and the Beebe at the northern edge are the best known of the Georgetown mines. The Alpine was first developed in the 1860's and was extensively worked during the 1930's. The Beebe is largely a twentieth-century development. Both produced occasional bonanza pay streaks but gold values were spotty. The Alpine shaft is less than 500 feet deep; the Beebe has a large open cut and a 500-foot shaft.

Five and one-half miles west of Georgetown is the crossroads hamlet of Greenwood which once boasted several wineries and was a supply center for many adjacent placer districts. A large lumber yard is the principal activity there now. Numerous placer and hydraulic diggings can be seen along the road between Georgetown and Greenwood. The bedrock is Mariposa slate and greenstone of uncertain age but there are few good exposures because of the deeply weathered nature of the bedrock and the soil mantle. The road is bordered by rank growths of yellow-flowering Spanish broom, an introduced plant.

A mile north of Greenwood at the Greens Mill road junction are good exposures of well bedded Mariposa slate. The relation of the bedding to the slaty cleavage can easily be seen there. A number of small folds within the Mariposa are evident in the road cuts along the Greens Mill road.

Less than half a mile from Greens Mill junction, a paved road turns off to the north which leads to Spanish Dry Diggin's and ultimately to other old camps on the North Fork of the American River. Spanish Dry Diggin's was discovered by a group of Spaniards under General Pico in 1848. The placer mines were soon superseded by the "seam" or stringer-load mines such as the Grit and the Barr. There has been a resumption of mining activity at the Grit or Littycote mine. The Grit had an early production of over $500,000 and the Barr over $300,000. A mass of gold weighing 201 troy ounces was taken from the Grit mine in August 1865. This was donated to the museum of the State Division of Mines in honor of Jules Fricot by his heir Mrs. Marie Fricot Berton and is now on exhibition in the Ferry Building, San Francisco.

One mile beyond the Greens Mill road junction is a fault contact between Calaveras rocks and serpentine. The Calaveras there is composed of mica schist, chert and basic intrusives such as basalt. Another small body of serpentine occurs at the Penobscot farm 1.3 miles farther west. From the Penobscot farm west to Cool the basement rocks are mainly Calaveras schist, chert, and meta-basalt and greenstones of doubtful age. These are intruded locally by small bodies of serpentine. The Penobscot farm is a picturesque, well kept property surrounded by orchards and grazing land and is the principal landmark between Greenwood and Cool.

Resuming the way up Highway 49 from Cool, the route is through serpentine and then along a narrow limestone belt bounded on both sides by greenstones of uncertain age. An enormous thickness of green meta-volcanics is exposed between the limestone quarries and Auburn. The North Fork of the American River has cut a tremendous gorge into this rock and the exposures in the river bed and the road cuts leading down to it are excellent. This meta-volcanic series may be a northern facies of the Logtown Ridge meta-volcanics but accurate correlation has not yet been established.

FIG. 27. Chert reef in Calaveras meta-sediments on the west side of Highway 49, 2.3 miles north of the South Fork of Wolf Creek, Nevada County.

FIG. 28. Glacial boulders in a deposit of till or glacial moraine on Highway 49 along Sardine Creek northeast of Sierra City, Sierra County.

FIG. 29. Outcrop of Mariposa slate near the Pacific Minerals Company slate quarry north of Placerville, El Dorado County.

FIG. 30. View southwest down the North Fork of the Yuba River in the vicinity of Indian Valley Camp in Sierra County.

FIG. 31. Potholed granodiorite bedrock along the South Fork of Yuba River close to the Highway 49 bridge, Nevada County.

FIG. 32. Springs and waterfalls emerging from glacio-fluvial deposits along Sardine Creek, Sierra County. The falls are close beside Highway 49.

A mile and a half north of Cool, a group of limestone quarries can be seen on the north side of the highway. Limestone was first quarried and burned there some 40 or 50 years ago by the Cave Valley Lime Company. One of the old kilns can be seen close to Highway 49 near the abandoned quarry, a quarter of a mile south of the road turnoff to the main workings. The kiln walls were made of limestone lined with greenstone. Local wood was used to fire the kilns. The present operators of the quarry, the California Rock and Gravel Company, quarry and crush the limestone for conversion into lump lime but do not produce either lime or cement themselves.

A mile beyond the limestone quarries, Highway 49 winds down to the bottom of the canyon of the North Fork of the American River. Both branches of the North Fork are deeply incised and transverse profiles appear youthful. However, an aerial view of the course of the river shows a series of broad intrenched meanders indicating that the pattern has been superimposed from an ancestral land surface and that the V-shaped transverse profile is produced by rejuvenation. Half a mile from the bridge, the junction of the North and Middle Forks of the American may be seen.

The American River bridge is at the El Dorado-Placer County line. The river is both wide and deep at this point and the effect of deep green water against green rocks is striking. The massive greenstones strike diagonally across the river and have been planed off and polished below high water mark. The railroad bridge and roadbed of the Pacific Portland Cement Company Railroad can be seen close to the highway bridge. This railroad formerly connected the limestone quarries along the American River with the Southern Pacific tracks at Auburn. The rails were removed during the last war. Beyond the bridge, the highway begins the ascent up the opposite canyon wall and continues on into Auburn. A new all-steel-and-concrete bridge has been recently completed to replace the old wood-and-steel structure.

Auburn, county seat of Placer County, was founded in 1848 as a rich placer mining camp. Present day Auburn consists of Old Auburn, with its "roaring '50's" look and numerous historical spots, and New Auburn, a modern up-to-date town. Auburn is one of few towns which have acted as county seat of two counties. Before Placer County was created from a portion of Sutter County in 1851, Auburn acted as county seat of Sutter County. Auburn has always been a transportation center and large lumber and cattle interests have long been connected with it. The De Witt army hospital is located north of town. Highway 40, which connects with Reno and other transcontinental points passes through Auburn and it is served by the Southern Pacific Railroad.

Three miles west of Auburn near Highway 40 is the Ophir mining district. Ophir, first known as Spanish Corral, was one of the main placer camps of Auburn ravine and has since been the main gold-quartz mining center of Placer County. Although little is left of the town, the orchard and vineyard landscape is attractive.

Six miles northeast of Auburn at Hotaling, near Clipper Gap, one of the earliest iron mining operations in California was located. Clipper Gap and Hotaling can be reached via Highway 20 east from Auburn. The Hotaling iron mine was located in 1857 but no ore was shipped until 1869. The deposit was in the form of lenses at the contact of granodiorite and a metamorphic series of probable Paleozoic age. The ore minerals were magnetite and hematite containing from 40 percent to 65 percent iron. A blast furnace was operated on the property between 1880 and 1885 using charcoal made locally and limestone mined near by. It produced thirty to thirty-five tons of pig iron daily. Although red and yellow ocher were shipped from the vicinity in the late 1920's for mineral paint, no attempt to exploit the lower grade ores for their iron content has been made since the turn of the century.

AUBURN TO NORTH SAN JUAN—MAP 8

Between Auburn and the Bear River, Highway 49 traverses rolling open grassland broken here and there by patches of brush and scrub trees. The somewhat monotonous landscape to the north of Auburn gives no inkling of the splendid scenery soon to be in evidence from Grass Valley to the end of Highway 49. The bedrock between Auburn and Grass Valley is mainly green meta-volcanics of doubtful age which have been intruded by irregular bodies of serpentine and by basic dikes of several types. Between the forks of Dry Creek a narrow belt of Calaveras meta-sediments begins which rather closely parallels Highway 49, on its west side, as far north as Rattlesnake Creek. The Calaveras rocks are mainly mica schist, chert, and limestone. There are large granodiorite intrusions near Grass Valley and the bedrock from Nevada City to North San Juan is principally of plutonic igneous rock approaching granodiorite in average composition. All the Quaternary stream and bench gravels have been worked for gold. Tertiary deposits are absent between Auburn and Grass Valley along the route of Highway 49. There are no mines of any consequence south of the Grass Valley district of which the Bullion claim of the Idaho-Maryland Mines Company, Ltd., is the southernmost member.

Highway 49 crosses the Bear River and the Placer-Nevada County line 8.7 miles north of Auburn. The vicinity of the Bear River bridge is of considerable geologic interest and is an attractive spot for fishing enthusiasts and pleasure seekers. A major thrust fault diagonally crosses the Highway in a NW-SE direction and the crumpled rocks along its trace are an interesting study. West of the bridge along the eastern bank of the river, the sheared and crumpled meta-volcanics are, in places, a lattice-work of silica-carbonate veinlets. Discontinuous, irregular bodies of serpentine appear along the contact, and the crumpled volcanics include fragments of chert and limestone. East of the bridge a few hundred yards, the massive greenstones contain amygdaloidal horizons and represent quiet lava flows rather than the pyroclastic beds seen to the west.

Two miles north of Bear River is Higgins Corner. A road connecting with the hamlet of Wolf leads off to the west and another to the east leads to the Combie Dam and Reservoir on Bear River. A prominent outcrop of Calaveras chert forms a reef just west of the highway 2.3 miles north of the south fork of Wolf Creek. This reef is almost vertical in attitude and is associated with greenstones of uncertain age. This is one of the few exposures of chert to be seen close to Highway 49 south of the Yuba River.

The Lime Kiln or Jones ranch was the site of a series of limestone quarries and kilns where lime for mortar was prepared at a very early date. Traces of the old workings have been almost obliterated, but partially burned limestone marks the old kiln sites. The limestone bodies are small and are now largely masked by the soil mantle. Chemical analysis of the limestone shows it to be of excellent grade. The Lime Kiln ranch is located three miles west of Highway 49 via dirt road. The turnoff is 5.3 miles north of Higgins Corners and is marked by a white sign.

Three miles beyond the chert reef the greenstone bedrock is invaded by granodiorite. The contact is plainly visible in a roadcut on the west side of the highway. The dark minerals in the granodiorite near the contact have been altered to chlorite and green amphiboles, and the granodiorite is almost as green as the meta-andesite series which it invades. A feldspar porphyry is present close to the contact which does not appear to be related to either the meta-volcanic series or the granodiorite, and may have been brought up from below by the intrusion. The porphyry is composed of abundant large plagioclase phenocrysts averaging 3 mm. in diameter set in a fine-grained black groundmass.

The change in bedrock from meta-volcanics to granodiorite is almost immediately reflected by the vegetation. Heavy growths of manzanita cover most of the granodiorite bedrock with a dense gray-green mantle. The manzanita thickets are most conspicuous in the vicinity of La Barr meadows.

Grass Valley is probably the most beautiful active mining camp in California. Mining camps the world over are notoriously ugly and uncomfortable places to live, but Grass Valley is set in a well watered coniferous forest of great beauty. Many stands of large trees have been spared the loggers axe and tower in dark green borders about broad meadowlands. The entire aspect of suburban Grass Valley is parklike. Even the mine dumps and buildings are more or less masked by trees so that the scenery suffers little by their presence. The business district of town is much like that of other Sierran towns.

Grass Valley is connected to the overland route through Reno via Highway 20 which joins Highway 40. A railroad once connected Nevada City and Grass Valley to the transcontinental route of the Southern Pacific but the tracks have been removed. Aside from explorations of Spanish Americans of which there is no record, Grass Valley was first visited by French emigrants in 1846. Gold miners from Oregon spent considerable time there in 1848 but the first permanent settlers who were emigrants from the east arrived in 1849. Historical spots in Grass Valley are numerous. The careers of such famous names as Lola Montez and Lotta Crabtree are closely associated with the history of the town. Its lode mines constitute the most productive group of gold properties in California and rank among the richest in the nation.

The geology of the Grass Valley mines differs greatly from that of the Mother Lode mines. Very little large scale faulting is in evidence in the Grass Valley district. The Mariposa slate is largely absent and even Calaveras rocks usually do not contain ore. The main veins dip on an average of 35° whereas most Mother Lode veins are steeply dipping. The minor cross veins are usually not mineralized except at their intersections with main veins. The wall rocks of the Idaho-Maryland and Spring Hill mines are principally gabbro and serpentine; those of the Empire Star and Golden Center are granodiorite, meta-andesite, diabase, and Calaveras schist. Vein forming minerals from the Grass Valley district include ankerite, native arsenic, arsenopyrite, chalcopyrite, chromite, epidote, galena, gold, magnetite, mariposite, pyrite, pyrrhotite, sphalerite, and rarely molybdenite, scheelite, hessite, and altaite. The latter two are tellurides of gold and lead respectively. Wall rocks in the district are heavily watered above the 1500 foot level and water flows into the lowermost workings necessitating use of elaborate pumping systems. Pumps which handle 3000 gallons per minute are used in the wettest spots. Although exceedingly humid, Grass Valley mines are among the coolest in the world. The temperature increase or geothermal gradient below ground is less than 1° F. per 100 feet of depth.

The largest mining operation in Grass Valley is that of the Empire-Star Mines Company, Ltd. The Empire-Star is a consolidation of the major North Star, Pennsylvania, and Empire mines and a host of lesser workings. The Empire has been operated continuously since 1851. Some of the other shafts have been shut down for short periods at various times since discovery. The workings of the Empire-Star total more than 200 miles in length making it one of the most widespread mines in existence. It has been mined to an inclined depth of more than 11,000 feet or a vertical depth of over a mile. The total production of the Empire-Star group has been in excess of $120,000,000. For the locations of the various shafts of the Empire-Star and other Grass Valley mines see the accompanying map.

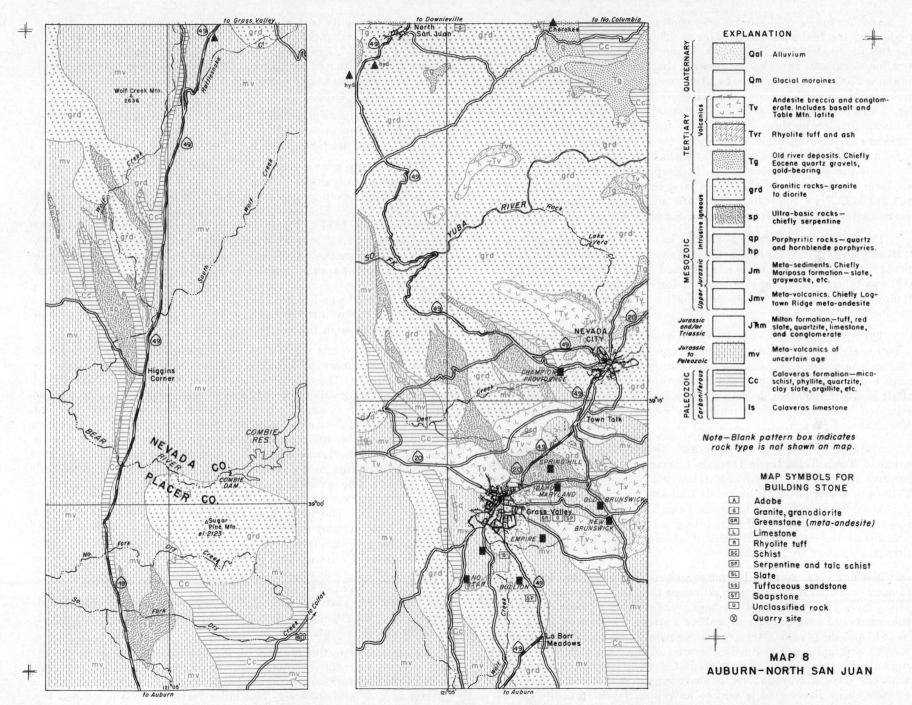

EXPLANATION

QUATERNARY	Qal	Alluvium
	Qm	Glacial moraines
TERTIARY Volcanics	Tv	Andesite breccia and conglomerate. Includes basalt and Table Mtn. latite
	Tvr	Rhyolite tuff and ash
	Tg	Old river deposits. Chiefly Eocene quartz gravels, gold-bearing
MESOZOIC Intrusive igneous	grd	Granitic rocks—granite to diorite
	sp	Ultra-basic rocks—chiefly serpentine
	qp hp	Porphyritic rocks—quartz and hornblende porphyries.
Upper Jurassic	Jm	Meta-sediments. Chiefly Mariposa formation—slate, graywacke, etc.
	Jmv	Meta-volcanics. Chiefly Logtown Ridge meta-andesite
Jurassic and/or Triassic	JŦm	Milton formation,—tuff, red slate, quartzite, limestone, and conglomerate
Jurassic to Paleozoic	mv	Meta-volcanics of uncertain age
PALEOZOIC Carboniferous	Cc	Calaveras formation—mica-schist, phyllite, quartzite, clay slate, argillite, etc.
	ls	Calaveras limestone

Note—Blank pattern box indicates rock type is not shown on map.

MAP SYMBOLS FOR BUILDING STONE

- A Adobe
- G Granite, granodiorite
- GR Greenstone (meta-andesite)
- L Limestone
- R Rhyolite tuff
- SC Schist
- SP Serpentine and talc schist
- SL Slate
- SS Tuffaceous sandstone
- ST Soapstone
- U Unclassified rock
- ⊗ Quarry site

MAP 8
AUBURN—NORTH SAN JUAN

Another major gold-mining operation in Grass Valley is being carried on by the Idaho-Maryland Mines Corporation. Its holdings include the Old Brunswick, New Brunswick, Idaho, and Eureka mines and many smaller workings. The New Brunswick shaft is 3450 feet deep and the Idaho is 2700 feet deep via shaft and winze. A successful attempt at shaft sinking by core drilling was made by the Idaho-Maryland. The Idaho No. 2 shaft was sunk 1000 feet into serpentine by this method using a Newsom drilling machine developed at the Idaho-Maryland. The drill cores are five feet in diameter and weigh several tons each. Many of these cores are piled about the entrance to the shaft. Although the Idaho-Maryland is not as large an operation as the Empire-Star, it is still among the six largest gold mines in California, and has a recorded production of $64,240,543. Very complete, up-to-date ore-treatment plants are connected with both Idaho-Maryland and Empire-Star mines.

The Golden Center mine is located in the heart of the business district of Grass Valley. Although the surface extent of the Golden Center property is not great the mine was rich and ore worth more than $2,500,-000 was taken from it before litigation forced a shut down. The Golden Center is currently idle. The deepest shaft is 1900 feet as measured along the incline.

The Spring Hill mine northeast of Grass Valley is a small but promising operation which is active at the present time. It is one of the neatest, best maintained properties in the gold country and its headframe and mill have been photographed repeatedly for various publications. The main shaft is about 1900 feet deep in diabase and serpentine wall rocks. The recorded production, most of which has been within the last 20 years, is $300,000.

Midway between Grass Valley and Nevada City is the old mining camp of Town Talk. Little remains to mark the site except a modern gasoline station and eating house. Historian Glasscock has it that Town Talk came about partly as an act of God and partly as a practical joke. An old saloon sign bearing the words Town Talk is supposed to have been stranded in the vicinity of the camp by flood waters of Deer Creek. Some wag fished the sign out and stuck it up on the hill and the camp was thereafter known by that name.

Nevada City, four miles northeast of Grass Valley, has been a famous lode-gold mining center although the mines there are currently idle. James Marshall passed through there seeking a placer bonanza in the summer of 1848 but missed making a strike. The first settlers arrived in 1849 and the placers attracted a large population within a few months. Known originally as Coyoteville, because of the local method of tunneling called coyoteing, the name Nevada City was evolved after a dispute with the state of Nevada over priority rights to that name. A total of $8,000,000 in placer gold is said to have been taken from the vicinity.

Nevada City is county seat of Nevada County and, like Grass Valley, is full of pioneer landmarks such as the Wells-Fargo Express Office site established in 1853, fire-houses built in the 1860's, and a remnant of Chinatown. It is situated on Highway 20, which connects with Reno and, like Grass Valley, was once connected to the transcontinental rail route of the Southern Pacific.

The principal lode mines of Nevada City are the Lava Cap, Murchie, Champion, and Providence. The Nevada City assay office is credited with assaying the first ore taken from the Comstock lode.

The Lava Cap mine has a recent history dating from 1933. In its ten years of operation it grossed about $12,000,000 in gold and silver! The mine is 2700 feet deep and has over five miles of lateral workings. The Murchie was worked in a small way in the 1890's but major production took place in the 1930's. The mine is now owned by the Empire Star Mines Company, Ltd., and is currently idle. It was an exceedingly productive mine before the last World War but few figures on it are available. The Champion and Providence mines have been worked discontinuously, with indifferent success, since the early day lode-mining period of the 1860's and 1870's. The Nevada City mines lie at the fringe of the Grass Valley district and the ore shoots have not persisted at depth as have those in the heart of the district.

West from Nevada City, Highway 49 passes through a thick series of Tertiary gravels which lie at the southern base of a ridge of rhyolite tuff and andesite. These deposits have been extensively hydraulicked and placered. Hydraulic pits and faces of moderate size can be seen on both sides of the highway. West of the gravels the granodiorite outcrops are full of dark inclusions or enclaves. These vary in size from fractions of an inch to one foot in diameter. Enclaves are common in many granitic batholiths and are formed either by magmatic segregation of various mineral constituents or by inclusion and partial assimilation of wall rocks caught in the invading magma. In most cases they carry a greater proportion of dark minerals than the matrix rock and have a somewhat different texture. The latter may be either finer or coarser than the including rock and may differ in many other ways. The enclaves west of Nevada City are unique in that they carry a large proportion of the mineral pyrite. Pyrite occurs only in the enclaves, not in the matrix rock, and probably was a constituent of the assimilated rock from which the enclaves formed. The texture is granitic but the crystals are finer than those in the matrix rock, which is essentially a biotite-hornblende granodiorite. Excellent exposures of these rocks may be seen in roadcuts 1.2 miles west of Nevada City.

Immediately west of the enclave locality is the contact between the granodiorite and meta-volcanic greenstones. Lindgren's map shows these to be in the Calaveras formation but separate from greenstones lying a quarter of a mile to the west. Two miles farther to the northwest is a narrow belt of serpentine and related basic intrusive rocks which are not particularly well exposed along the highway except in deeply weathered roadcuts. Deeply weathered areas and dark-red soil mark remnants of the old Eocene surface. The remainder of the route into North San Juan lies on a granitic bedrock ranging in composition from quartz diorite to granodiorite. A small roof pendant or remnant of overlying wall rock of dark green amphibolite can be seen in roadcuts 1.2 miles south of the Yuba River bridge. The greenstone is cut by aplite and pegmatite dikes. A good locality for collecting hornblende crystals is to be seen close to the amphibolite contact.

Close to the south abutment of the Yuba River bridge, a broad roadcut and quarry in granodiorite afford an excellent close-up view of the intruding batholith. The coarse matrix is full of large inclusions or enclaves and several prominent joint systems prevail which have aided in quarrying the rock for fill. The scenic gorge of the South Fork of the Yuba is well worth seeing. The river water is often discolored by tailings from hydraulic workings upstream.

The road cuts up the grade along the north wall of the Yuba River canyon expose granitic rocks of at least two separate intrusive bodies. Contacts between the intrusions are indistinct, granodiorite grading into darker hornblende diorite which is cut by light-colored dikes of variable texture.

In the vicinity of Shady Creek bridge extensive deposits of Quaternary gravels choke the river bed. These are partly the result of placer operations connected with Tertiary gravels situated upstream.

One mile northwest of Shady Creek bridge an unpaved road intersects Highway 49 which connects with the hydraulic mines of Cherokee, North Columbia, North Bloomfield, Relief, Omega and many others. The Cherokee diggings are six miles northeast of the above intersection, North Columbia is a little over nine miles, and North Bloomfield is about 19 miles. The immensity of the North Bloomfield pits must be seen to be believed. Although excavated entirely by powerful jets of water, the pits compare favorably in size with many of the open pit copper and iron mines of other states which have been excavated by modern mechanical means. The Malakoff pit west of North Bloomfield resembles a miniature Bryce Canyon. The soft clay and gravel walls have been fluted and otherwise sculptured by erosion into "badlands" of great charm. The pastel-colored horizons in the pit gravels contrast strikingly with the deep red soil mantle and the dark-green backdrop of forest trees. Some idea of the achievement of the nineteenth-century hydraulic miners in moving such great quantities of material without modern equipment may be had from the following figures: 20,000,000 cu. yds. were excavated at North Bloomfield; and 25,000,000 cu. yds. from North Columbia. Only 14 percent of the gravel reserves at North Columbia had been removed by the time hydraulic mining was stopped by court injunction in 1884. The problem of the debris from such operations was, of course, a great one. It choked the rivers below and ruined riverbottom lands for farming purposes. In some places the problem has been solved by building debris dams; in others by selective spreading of waste on already valueless areas. A few hydraulic mines such as Relief and Omega situated southeast of North Bloomfield are currently in operation, but most have been idle since the 1880's.

Petersons Corner, 1.2 miles northwest of the North Columbia-Highway 49 intersection is the terminus of a paved road connecting with the hydraulic-mining towns of Sweetland, Birchville, French Corral, and Bridgeport. An interesting and a scenic sidetrip on this road will bring one out on Highway 20 at Bitney Corner a few miles west of Nevada City. The route lies principally through granitic basement rocks which have been deeply weathered into a lateritic red clay in many places. An occasional belt of black or green meta-volcanics may be seen bordered on either side by granitic rocks. The many Tertiary gravel deposits lying on this surface are the basis for the once thriving hydraulic mines.

Sweetland, of which Petersons Corner is a part, was originally a placer-mining camp first settled in the early 1850's. Together with adjoining towns to the southwest, Sweetland was a going and prosperous town until the ban on hydraulicking took away the principal source of income of the region. Sweetland is now a handful of frame dwellings set in a quiet country landscape. Birchville, 1.5 miles southwest of Sweetland, is located principally by the hydraulic pits to the north of the old town site. Several are filled with water and form small lakes.

Three miles below Birchville is French Corral which dates from 1849. The town is located in an attractive valley on a tributary to the South Fork of the Yuba River. Several well preserved stone and brick buildings remain along the main street. French Corral was at one end of the first long distance telephone line ever built. It connected with Birchville, Sweetland, North San Juan, Cherokee, North Columbia, North Bloomfield and Bowman or French Lake, a distance of 58 miles.

Very little remains at the Yuba River site of Bridgeport, three miles southwest of French Corral. A covered wooden bridge spans the river and red ranch buildings remain inside stone-walled corrals. A partly overgrown graveyard is located beside the road a short distance south of the river. There is little of particular geologic or historical interest between Bridgeport and Bitney Corner on Highway 20, but the landscape is an attractive one and the side route will draw travelers who like to keep off the beaten track.

North along Highway 49 from Petersons Corner, remnants of the exhumed Eocene surface are evident in several places. This flat surface is particularly noticeable in the vicinity of North San Juan. Large hydraulic diggings can be seen to the west. The granitic basement rocks are a dark or melanistic phase of the ordinarily light-colored granodiorite, being rich in biotite mica.

North San Juan is one of the largest and best preserved of the northern gold towns. The iron grillwork on the old brick buildings resembles the grilled balconies of the Vieux Carré or French quarter of New Orleans. North San Juan was founded about 1853 not by Spanish Californians, as the name suggests, but by Christian Kientz, an immigrant of German ancestry. He thought the hill resembled another known as San Juan and named the new spot accordingly.

NORTH SAN JUAN TO DOWNIEVILLE—MAP 9

The topography along Highway 49 north of North San Juan becomes increasingly rugged and more and more typical of the higher Sierra. The northward trend to the highway changes north of Camptonville and the route follows the bottom of the tremendous canyon of the North Fork of the Yuba in a broad northeasterly arc. Remnants of the Eocene surface become more and more restricted in areal extent and are commonly perched well over a thousand feet above present main-stream gradients. Calaveras meta-sediments and thick sections of greenstones reappear south of Camptonville and granitic rocks outcrop in only one area between Camptonville and Downieville. Except for logged-off areas of limited extent in the vicinity of North San Juan and Camptonville, the entire region is heavily forested with coniferous trees. The fauna and flora are typical of the upper transition and lower Canadian life zones. The dominant forest trees are yellow pines and Douglas firs (Oregon pines) with lesser numbers of white firs, incense cedars, and western hemlocks. Alders and other water-loving trees grow along the water courses.

Two and eight tenths miles north of North San Juan the highway crosses the Middle Fork of the Yuba at the Yuba County line. The granodiorite near the bridge is prominently jointed into rectangular blocks. One tenth of a mile beyond the bridge, a dirt road branches off to the east at an acute angle to the highway and recrosses the Yuba over a covered wooden bridge much like the one at Bridgeport. It is covered as a protection against the winter snow pack and the tunnel-like appearance is typical of old mountain bridges in this region. The road connects with the famous mining district of Alleghany, located 24 miles northeast of the turnoff. Alleghany can also be reached via dirt road from Goodyears Bar, a few miles west of Downieville. Neither road is readily passable in wet or snowy weather and a visit to Alleghany should only be attempted by those used to back country roads. Lode, drift, and hydraulic mines are located in the vicinity of Alleghany many of which have fine production records.

The Ruby drift mine is famous for its coarse gold nuggets and its large quartz crystals. It is one of but few mines in the district which are still operating. The workings are principally tunnels in the bedrock from which raises are put up to the channel gravels above. There are several miles of tunnels and drifts and several vertical access and escapeway shafts. Ore is hauled out along the main tunnel level and run through sluices. More than 123 nuggets valued at over $100.00 each had been removed from the Ruby by 1941. The largest weighed 52.3 ounces and was worth $1,758.00.

The best known lode mines in the Alleghany district are the Sixteen-to-One, Oriental, Plumbago, Rainbow, and Bush Creek, all of which have recorded productions in the millions of dollars. Dozens of smaller workings have been profitable from time to time. The Brush Creek and Yellow Jacket mines were operating early in 1948 as well as the major Sixteen-to-One.

The Sixteen-to-One, located a short distance downhill toward Kanaka Creek from the town of Alleghany, has been the principal producer of the district. It was discovered in 1876 and, as now operated, is a consolidation of the Twenty-One and Tightner mines and several miscellaneous properties. The main vein system lies along a reverse fault in wall rocks of hornblende schist and other metamorphosed sediments of the Tightner and Kanaka members of the Calaveras formation. Serpentine dikes cut the Calaveras and both are cut by the thrust system. Vein minerals from the Sixteen-to-One include arsenopyrite, mariposite, sphalerite, gold, graphite, chalcopyrite, quartz, ankerite, tetrahedrite, galena, pyrrhotite, and pyrite. The deepest part of the mine is 3300 feet from the surface as measured along the inclined Tightner shaft. The total recorded production of the Sixteen-to-One is slightly in excess of $16,100,000.

Hydraulicking in the Alleghany district was confined to a few favorable locations where the gravels were not deeply buried under the Tertiary lava cap. Ferguson has estimated that between two and four million dollars were extracted from the district by hydraulic means. Something in excess of $10,000,000 was produced from drift mines such as the Ruby and about $28,000,000 from lode mines. Placer gravels, principally of Quaternary age added over a million dollars to the above totals, giving a grand total of over $38,000,000 for all gold mines in the district. Ferguson and Gannett give another interesting sidelight on the richness of the Alleghany lodes. They compiled, from various authorities, a table of the probable amounts of gold eroded from the Alleghany lodes and redeposited in channel gravels below. These estimates ranged from $18,000,000 to $52,000,000.

The placer and hydraulic town of Camptonville is located half a mile off Highway 49, 8.4 miles northeast of North San Juan. Camptonville was founded about 1850 as a hostelry on the Nevada City-Downieville road. The town boomed as the result of local gold discoveries in 1852. Few present-day buildings date back to gold rush days as the town was destroyed several times by fire. However, a quasi-colonial type

FIG. 33. View northeast toward old Omega hydraulic mine, Nevada County.
Photo by Olaf P. Jenkins.

FIG. 35. Another view of the Omega hydraulic pit showing coarse cobbles in the foreground, the finer parts of the deposit having been washed away by the hose nozzles. *Photo by Olaf P. Jenkins.*

FIG. 34. Looking north toward hydraulic pit at North Bloomfield. The excavations which once were thought to be an eyesore are now places of great beauty. *Photo by Olaf P. Jenkins.*

FIG. 36. Joubert hydraulic pits in Sierra County. Highway 49 runs directly through these diggings. *Photo by Olaf P. Jenkins.*

FIG. 37. Sierra Buttes, a group of volcanic remnants, as seen from the foot of Yuba Pass, Sierra County, looking southwest. *Photo by C. V. Averill.*

FIG. 39. The California Rock and Gravel Company limestone quarry on the south side of the Middle Fork of the American River east of Auburn. *Photo by Olaf P. Jenkins.*

FIG. 38. A group of "tombstone rocks," the eroded tilted edges of meta-volcanics of the Logtown Ridge formation, exposed along the road near Campo Seco. *Photo by Olaf P. Jenkins.*

FIG. 40. Spheroidal weathering in massive granodiorite of Ebbetts Pass road west of Calaveras Big Trees. Spheroids such as this may be seen along Highway 49 in Yuba Pass between Sierra City and Sattley. *Photo by Olaf P. Jenkins.*

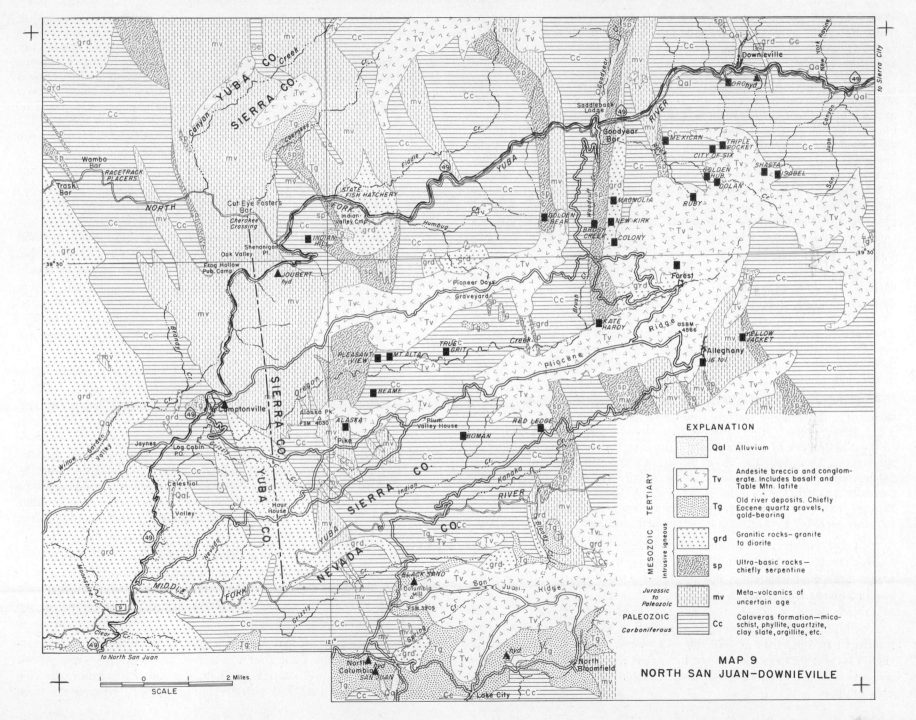

EXPLANATION

| | Qal | Alluvium |

MESOZOIC / TERTIARY — Intrusive igneous

	Tv	Andesite breccia and conglomerate. Includes basalt and Table Mtn. latite
	Tg	Old river deposits. Chiefly Eocene quartz gravels, gold-bearing
	grd	Granitic rocks— granite to diorite
	sp	Ultra-basic rocks— chiefly serpentine

Jurassic to Paleozoic

| | mv | Meta-volcanics of uncertain age |

PALEOZOIC — Carboniferous

| | Cc | Calaveras formation—mica-schist, phyllite, quartzite, clay slate, argillite, etc. |

MAP 9
NORTH SAN JUAN–DOWNIEVILLE

of architecture prevails among the older frame buildings and the large frame hotel is a delightful spot shaded by large trees. Red, pock-marked, Eocene gravels outcrop on the hills to the northeast of town much as the gold diggers left them.

Half a mile below the Camptonville turnoff, a group of pegmatite and aplite dikes stand out of the deeply weathered bedrock. The light colored minerals of the dikes show little evidence of weathering whereas the biotite-rich matrix is decomposed. Half a mile above the Camptonville road deeply weathered cleavable meta-volcanics can be seen lying below the deep red soil mantle and below Tertiary gravel deposits. The meta-volcanics are so decomposed that they disintegrate when tapped with a hammer. Few places so clearly illustrate the relationship between the deeply weathered rocks of the Eocene surface, the Eocene channel gravels, and the present-day land surface. The road cuts are also an excellent study in direct formation of soil mantle from parent bedrock lying immediately below.

Between Camptonville and the Frog Hollow public camp, several small bodies of deeply weathered granite rock outcrop along the roadside. These approximate a gabbro in composition and were apparently too small to be mapped by the early members of the Geological Survey. They mapped this entire area as amphibolite but this designation covers a wide variety of rock types including fine grained basic and intermediate intrusives, green meta-volcanics, mica schist, and the aforementioned gabbro.

Frog Hollow, three miles north of Camptonville, is the first of a series of public camps scattered along or near the North Fork of the Yuba River. Frog Hollow is on Willow Creek which is not a tributary to the North Fork of the Yuba but runs into Bullards Bar reservoir to the west of Camptonville. These public camps lie in a naturalist's and fisherman's paradise and are likewise good base camps for the geologically minded. The 36 miles between Frog Hollow and Sierra City lies through excellent outcroppings of a wide range of igneous and metamorphic rocks of great interest to petrologists and rock lovers of all kinds.

In the vicinity of the Joubert hydraulic diggings, the highway crosses from Yuba to Sierra County. Sierra County is famous for the many large gold nuggets it has produced. One from the Monumental mine at Sierra Buttes weighed 1596 oz. troy, worth $17,654. The placers of French Ravine produced four nuggets which weighed from 93 to 532 oz. each. Henry G. Hanks in his compilation of famous gold nuggets published in 1882 lists no less than 13 Sierra County nuggets among the 83 largest produced in the world to that date. The Ruby mine, previously mentioned in connection with Alleghany, is still producing sizeable nuggets.

Highway 49 passes through the heart of the Joubert hydraulic diggings and the Eocene gravels and clays can be studied there at close range. The Joubert deposits contain a large percentage of white clay which would be valuable if it could be separated from admixed gravels. Some areas are of almost pure white clay. Other parts of the deposit have off-colored clays ranging from deep red to lavender. Clay deposits are present in association with many other Eocene gravel deposits of Nevada, Yuba, and Sierra Counties, but to date, the only clays of the Sierran foothills that are being worked are at the edge of the Sacramento Valley, principally in the vicinity of Ione, Amador County.

A splendid panorama up the V-shaped canyon of the Yuba may be seen 2.6 miles northeast of Joubert just before the highway descends to the level of the river. Youthful stream profiles may be seen at other points along the highway between Joubert and Downieville.

A thick series of partially metamorphosed volcanic rocks is exposed in the vicinity of the highway bridge over the North Fork of the Yuba. Amygdaloidal flows, agglomerates and tuffs may be seen in various stages of metamorphism some completely recrystallized to schist and others partially altered. Metallic minerals such as magnetite are disseminated in the lavas along the dirt road leading off to the north of the bridge. Good parking places may be had along this road and exposures are good along the river and in places along the road.

Indian Valley public camp, the second of a series of excellent campsites beside the river, is located two miles east of the bridge. Half a mile before reaching the camp is the granodiorite-meta-volcanic contact. The granodiorite, which is well exposed in a quarry east of Indian Valley camp, is much like the average granodiorite south of Camptonville. The belt of serpentine which appears on the map is not evident from the highway. The granodiorite intrusion is 1.7 miles wide along the highway. One mile west of Ramshorn Creek bridge is a good exposure of gray-green chert associated with phyllite and meta-volcanics. Another public camp is located at the junction of Ramshorn Creek with the North Fork of the Yuba.

Midway between Ramshorn Creek and Goodyears Bar, good views of the columnarly jointed basalt of Bald Top Mountain may be seen to the north. The Bald Top and adjacent lavas represent the latest period of Sierran volcanism with the possible exception of some flows on the east side of the range.

Goodyears Bar, located near the junction of Woodruff and Goodyear Creeks with the Yuba four miles west of Downieville, was settled in the summer of 1849. It prospered during the 1850's before its rich placers were exhausted, but a fire which virtually destroyed the town in 1864 culminated a steady decline which had begun some years earlier. A good dirt road from the Alleghany mining district joins Highway 49 in the vicinity of Goodyears Bar.

Three-tenths of a mile east of Goodyears Bar is a prominent outcropping of serpentine which is associated with fine-grained dark intrusive rocks. Half a mile east of the serpentine belt is a small area of meta-gabbro. The fine-grained basic rocks are cut by quartz veins.

A broad zone of faulting and deformation is visible along the highway 1.4 miles west of Downieville. The meta-volcanics there are much contorted and, in many places, are impregnated with pyrite. In the stream bed below, deep circular depressions known as potholes or kettles may be seen in the exposed bedrock. Potholes are formed by the eddying, spinning action of rapid water over uneven, bare rock. Gravel and pebbles caught in the depressions are spun by the currents and aid in the circular downcutting effect. They are a common feature along streams of considerable gradient.

Downieville, county seat of Sierra County, is situated at the junction of the north and east branches of the North Fork of the Yuba River. Lofty tree-covered mountains surround it on all sides and it is a fitting location for the center of a well named county. There is very little flat land in the county and this is located either along river bottoms or on upland remnants of the Eocene surface. Like Goodyears Bar, Downieville was found in 1849 by a party of gold seekers. Originally known as The Forks, the name was changed to Downieville in honor of William Downie, one of the initial settlers. More than 5000 people jammed the town in 1851 and some rich strikes were made. So determined were the miners to get the gold from the bed of the Yuba that they flumed and diverted the river from its bed between Downieville and Goodyears Bar. This worked beautifully as long as summer held out, but winter floods quickly wiped out the project. After the placer mines were exhausted, gold mining went on in hydraulic, drift and a few lode mines. The town is now supported by lumber and mining interests and by Forest Service men. Very few historical buildings remain, the County Courthouse and St. Charles Hotel having burned in 1947. The Pioneer Museum, a well-built stone building with iron doors and window shutters, was restored by the heirs of pioneer J. M. B. Meroux and dedicated to the Pioneers of Sierra County by the Native Sons and Daughters of the Golden West in 1932. Costa's grocery store, also of stone, dates from 1852.

FIG. 41. Penn copper-zinc mine near Campo Seco, Calaveras County. *Photo by C. V. Averill.*

FIG. 42. Stamp mill near Jamestown, Tuolumne County, used for concentrating chrome ore. *Photo by C. V. Averill.*

DOWNIEVILLE TO SATTLEY—MAP 10

The northeastern end of Highway 49 lies along the headwaters of the North Fork of the North Fork of the Yuba and then climbs out of the Yuba drainage system and over Yuba Pass to the broad upland of Sierra Valley. Yuba Pass does not show the tremendous alpine landscape that is so typical of the passes to the south such as Tioga and Sonora. The greatest relief to be seen on Highway 49 is along the route from Camptonville to Sierra City. However, the end of the route is through heavily forested country full of streams, and the beauty of the woodlands partly compensates for the comparative lack of alpine features.

Immediately east of Downieville the roadcuts are in a belt of black slates which have been quarried for local use as a building stone. The slates are full of quartz veinlets which have invaded the series along the bedding planes. These slates closely resemble the Mariposa slates of the Mother Lode but have been assigned to the Calaveras formation by H. W. Turner. Quartz veins varying in width from fractions of an inch to two feet cut the country rock in many places along the road from Downieville to Sierra City. Although barren for the most part, some of these veins have been found to carry pocket gold. Several prospect holes close to quartz veins can be seen on the south side of the river. Granodiorite outcrops in several places in this vicinity and the quartz veins were undoubtedly derived from adjacent or underlying granitic intrusions.

Camp Yuba, 5.4 miles east of Downieville, is another of the very fine public camps situated on the banks of the river. This camp is near the old placer camp site of China Flat. Several lode-gold mines are located both to the northeast and southeast of Camp Yuba but none have been very successful. The rocks along the highway between Camp Yuba and the Ladies Canyon bridge include a small body of weathered granodiorite which looks as if pre-existing wall rocks had been assimilated by it. It is a dark, impure rock resembling a granite in texture only. Excellent examples of hill creep or false folding in platy meta-sediments may be seen along the roadside in several places. Hill creep is produced on steep slopes by gravitational bending of inclined strata in a downhill direction and is usually the result of downhill movement of the soil mantle which lies above the tilted edges of the stratified bedrock.

Between Ladies Canyon and Sierra City a wide variety of interbedded meta-sediments, meta-volcanics and dike-like intrusives are exposed in the many roadcuts. Slate, phyllite, schist, chert, quartz porphyry, serpentine, and green meta-volcanics can all be collected at various places along the highway. Terrace alluvium perched high above the present stream channel may be seen in the vicinity of Fournier Ranch and Loganville.

At the edge of Sierra City, a road leads off to the north which connects with the Sierra Buttes mining district. As mentioned in preceding paragraphs, the Sierra Buttes district is noted for the many large nuggets recovered there in early days. There is little or no activity in the district at present. The columnarly jointed lava cap of Sierra Buttes can be seen in many places along the highway in the vicinity of Sierra City.

Sierra City, located at the foot of towering peaks on a narrow river terrace, was first settled in 1850 by gold miners. The vicinity was full of Indian rancherias or camp sites and apparently was one of the most heavily populated Indian districts in California. The new settlement was destroyed by an avalanche in 1852 and the present buildings date from the 1860's or later. The main street of Sierra City resembles those of many other towns of the gold country. The brick-and-frame Busch Building has the same iron doors and shutters that are so typical of fire-conscious towns built in the 60's and 70's. Sierra City is famous for being the birthplace of a roisterous society known as E. Clampus Vitus. The organization has the reputation of being principally a perpetrator of practical jokes upon the uninitiated. At any rate, name and reputation are colorfully connected with the history of Sierran gold mining from Sierra City far down the Mother Lode. The society was reorganized several years ago by the California Historical Society, apparently with satisfactory results to all concerned.

East of Sierra City, Highway 49 passes close beside an east-west contact between the quartz-porphyry bedrock and overlying glacial moraine detritus. This is the first appearance of glacial debris along Highway 49 but morainal deposits can be seen in a great many places between Sierra City and Bassett at the foot of Yuba Pass. The most obvious characteristic of the glacial deposits is their extreme variability or heterogeneity. Clays, gravel, and huge boulders both stratified and unstratified are dumped together in irregularly shaped deposits. Some of the fragments or clasts have been planed off or faceted by the ice. Others have been grooved or striated by being ground against resistant bedrock. Most of the boulders and smaller stones are merely rounded or subangular and one must examine many of them to find any which have characteristic glacial markings. The quartz porphyry east of Sierra City is a light-buff rock with a very fine-grained groundmass and numerous small, rounded, quartz crystals or phenocrysts and less numerous rectangular or lath-shaped feldspar phenocrysts. The rock is probably close to a dacite in over-all composition. East of the quartz porphyry belt is a narrower belt of green porphyritic meta-andesite breccia much like the Logtown Ridge formation along the Mother Lode.

A road connecting with Gold Lake, Sardine Creek public camp and other parts of the Plumas National Forest joins Highway 49 4.3 miles northeast of Sierra City. Sardine Lake and others in the vicinity are cirque lakes of glacial origin. Except for the moraines to be seen along the North Fork of the Yuba, glacial features are few along Highway 49 and it is necessary to take side trips in order to see examples of glacial topography. A road passable in summer connects with the glacial Packer Lake

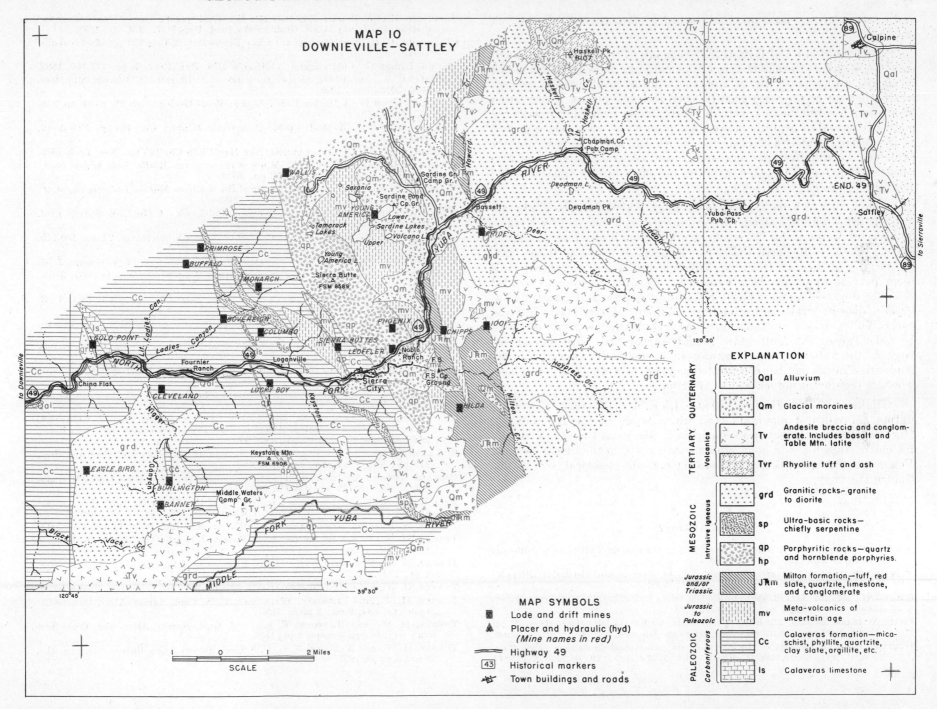

MAP 10
DOWNIEVILLE-SATTLEY

EXPLANATION

QUATERNARY

Qal — Alluvium

Qm — Glacial moraines

TERTIARY — Volcanics

Tv — Andesite breccia and conglomerate. Includes basalt and Table Mtn. latite

Tvr — Rhyolite tuff and ash

MESOZOIC — Intrusive igneous

grd — Granitic rocks—granite to diorite

sp — Ultra-basic rocks—chiefly serpentine

qp hp — Porphyritic rocks—quartz and hornblende porphyries.

Jurassic and/or Triassic

JℝM — Milton formation—tuff, red slate, quartzite, limestone, and conglomerate

Jurassic to Paleozoic

mv — Meta-volcanics of uncertain age

PALEOZOIC — Carboniferous

Cc — Calaveras formation—mica-schist, phyllite, quartzite, clay slate, argillite, etc.

ls — Calaveras limestone

MAP SYMBOLS

Lode and drift mines

Placer and hydraulic (hyd) (Mine names in red)

Highway 49

43 — Historical markers

Town buildings and roads

SCALE
1   0   1   2 Miles

and resorts. Sardine Lake must be reached by foot from Sardine Creek public camp.

From the vicinity of Bassett to the summit of the pass, the basement rocks are weathered granodiorites of the main pluton or batholith which forms the core of the Sierras. Spheroidal decay boulders can be seen weathering out of the main granitic mass in many places. Preservation of more or less unaltered spheroids in an almost completely weathered matrix is typical of granitic masses in a great many other places as well as the Sierras, and is a phenomenon which has never been adequately explained. Local differences in grain size and mineral composition sometimes account for it. In other instances the effect has no apparent local control.

The summit of Yuba Pass, at an elevation of 6701 feet, lies in a broad, upland valley which is slowly being dissected at either end by streams of opposing watersheds. The winding grade from Yuba Pass to Sattley affords fine views of Sierra Valley which opens out to the northeast from the vicinity of Sierraville. Sierra Valley is a graben or depressed fault block part of which has been masked by volcanic mountains extruded since the depression of the block. Subsequent erosion and glaciation has greatly dissected the disrupting lava. William Morris Davis believed Sierra Valley to be a continuation of the graben which is partly occupied by Lake Tahoe. The fault which roughly corresponds with the western edge of the valley crosses Highway 49 immediately west of Sattley. Andesitic gravels can be seen faulted against the granodiorite in places where the contact is not masked by alluvium.

Highway 49 joins Highway 89 at Sattley, Sierra County, thus terminating 277 miles of mountain road which began at the Highway 49-Highway 120 road junction at Mariposa in Mariposa County. Virtually the entire streach lies in gold mining country within the Sierra Nevada. Few routes through California are as replete with historical color as this Golden Highway.

BIBLIOGRAPHY

AVERILL, CHARLES V., and others, Placer mining for gold in California: California Div. Mines Bull. 135, 377 pp., 1946.

AVERILL, CHARLES V., Strategic minerals of the Sacramento district, California: California Div. Mines Rept. 39, pp. 71-76, 1943.

CALIFORNIA MINERS ASSOCIATION, California mines and minerals: California Miners Association, 445 pp., San Francisco, 1899.

DAVIS, WILLIAM MORRIS, The lakes of California: California Div. Mines Rept. 29, pp. 175-238, 1933 . . . California Jour. Mines and Geology, vol. 44, pp. 201-242, 1948.

DURRELL, CORDELL, Geology of the quartz crystal mines near Mokelumne Hill, Calaveras County, California: California Div. Mines Rept. 40, pp, 423-433, 1944.

FERGUSON, HENRY G. and GANNETT, R. W., Gold quartz veins of the Allaghany district, California: U. S. Geol. Survey Prof. Paper 172, 136 pp., 1932.

GLASSCOCK, C. B., A golden highway: The Bobbs-Merrill Co., 313 pp., Indianapolis, 1934.

HANKS, HENRY G., Gold nuggets: California Min. Bur. Rept. 2, pp. 147-150, 1882.

HAUSMANN, A., and others, Copper resources of California: California Min. Bur. Bull. 50, 275 pp., 1908.

HULIN, CARLTON D., A Mother Lode gold ore: Econ. Geology, vol. 23, no. 4, pp. 348-355, June 1930.

JACKSON, JOSEPH H., Anybody's gold: D. Appleton-Century Co., 445 pp., New York, 1941.

JACKSON, JOSEPH H., Tintypes in gold: The MacMillan Co., 191 pp., New York, 1939.

JULIHN, C. E., and HORTON, F. W., Mines of the southern Mother Lode region, pt. 1: U. S. Bur. Mines Bull. 413, 136 pp., 1938.

JULIHN, C. E. and HORTON, F. W., Mines of the southern Mother Lode region, pt. 2: U. S. Bur. Mines Bull. 424, 173 pp., 1940.

KNOPF, ADOLPH, The Mother Lode system of California: U. S. Geol. Survey Prof. Paper 157, 85 pp., 1929.

LAWSON, A. C., The Sierra Nevada: California Univ. Chronicle, vol. 23, pp. 130-149, 1921.

LINDGREN, WALDEMAR, U. S. Geol. Survey, Colfax folio (no. 66), 12 pp., 4 maps, 1897.

LINDGREN, WALDEMAR, U. S. Geol. Survey Atlas, Sacramento folio (no. 5), 5 pp., 4 maps, 1894.

LINDGREN, WALDEMAR, The Tertiary gravels of the Sierra Nevada, California: U. S. Geol. Survey Prof. Paper 73, 222 pp., 1911.

LINDGREN, WALDEMAR and TURNER, H. W., Placerville folio (no. 3), 5 pp., 4 maps, 1894.

LOGAN, CLARENCE A., The Mother Lode gold belt of California: California Div. Mines Bull. 108, 240 pp., 1934.

LOGAN, CLARENCE A., Tuolumne County: California Div. Mines Rept. 24, pp. 3-53, 1928.

RANSOME, F. L., U. S. Geol. Survey Atlas, Mother Lode district folio (no. 63), 11 pp., 8 maps, 1897.

RENSCH, H. E., RENSCH, E. G., and HOOVER, M. B., Historic spots in California, Valley and Sierra Counties: Stanford Univ. Press and Cambridge Univ. Press, 568 pp., Palo Alto and Cambridge, 1933.

RICKARD, THOMAS A., A history of American mining: McGraw-Hill Book Co., Inc., 419 pp., New York and London, 1932.

RICKARD, THOMAS A., The reopening of old mines along the Mother Lode: Min. and Sci. Press, vol. 112, pp. 935-939, 1916.

TALIAFERRO, NICHOLAS L., Manganese deposits of the Sierra Nevada; their genesis and metamorphism: California Div. Mines Bull. 125, pp. 277-332, 1943.

TUCKER, W. BURLING, Amador County: California Min. Bur. Rept. 14, pp. 3-54, 1914.

TURNER, H. W., U. S. Geol. Survey Atlas, Bidwell Bar folio (no. 43), 8 pp., 3 maps, 1 pl., 1898.

TURNER, H. W., U. S. Geol. Survey Atlas, Downieville folio (no. 37), 10 pp., 4 maps, 1 pl., 1897.

TURNER, H. W., U. S. Geol. Survey Atlas, Jackson folio (no. 11), 8 pp., 4 maps, 1894.

TURNER, H. W., and LINDGREN, WALDEMAR, U. S. Geol. Survey Atlas, Smartsville folio (no. 18), 8 pp., 4 maps, 1895.

TURNER, H. W., and RANSOME, F. L., U. S. Geol. Survey Atlas, Big Trees folio (no. 51), 10 pp., 3 maps, 1 pl., 1898.

TURNER, H. W., and RANSOME, F. L., U. S. Geol. Survey Atlas, Sonora folio (no. 41), 9 pp., 4 maps, 1897.

THE FORMATION OF QUARTZ VEINS

By John A. Burgess

How are quartz veins formed? This is a question that is frequently asked of geologists, and the answer is not altogether an easy one. Geologists ask it of themselves and in trying to explain it come out with answers that are different in some respects. The differences, however, are of a kind that are of more interest to the geologist than to those not engaged in that profession. The subject is a broad one; books have been written on it; and in order not to cover too much ground this short discussion will refer especially to veins of the Mother Lode of California. There are other types of veins to which it does not wholly apply. It should be made clear that in this brief essay only the high spots of the subject can be touched upon.

The things we know about quartz veins are the features that can be seen at the surface and in mines of which only a few are over a mile deep. We know the appearance of the veins, their general form, the materials and minerals of which they are composed, the arrangement of the minerals within them, and to a considerable extent the reactions between the substances that formed the vein and the rocks on its borders. The parts of the vein that we now see were formed deep below a pre-existing surface from which thousands of feet have been stripped by erosion, and they doubtless extend several miles below the present surface. Veins at the Argonaut and the Kennedy mines at Jackson were worked to more than a mile in depth without showing any change in their character. It is within this range that we have definite knowledge of the veins.

Among the things of which we have no positive knowledge are the depth to which the fissures extend, and the depth to which quartz continues in the fissures. Nor do we know the character of the rocks where the fissures terminate. These are features of the form and structure of the veins. And among the processes of vein formation, we do not know how the vein fissures were forced open to accommodate veins of the width that are found on the Mother Lode, nor do we know the source of the water that arose in the fissures to form the veins. There is not sufficient evidence from which to deduce with certainty how these things came about; but, short of certainty, there are reasonable explanations of how they could have happened.

It is estimated that the veins were formed over a hundred million years ago, and at great depths below what was then the surface of the earth. Obviously no one has seen a vein in the process of formation. Nevertheless geologists must face the problem and try to explain the origin of veins. This is done by reasoning from known facts to the unknown factors. The conclusions reached in this way give us all that can be expected under the circumstances; that is, reasonable explanations of the origin of the veins.

The deductions on which the leading geologists agree are: The veins are formed in deep fissures that extended to a zone of hot igneous rocks newly solidified, or partly solidified, from a molten condition. The gold in the veins is derived from these hot or molten rocks. It is known that molten rock, called magma, has a considerable quantity of water in its composition; in fact the magma is fluid not only because of its heat but also because of the presence of water. As the magma cools and hardens this water is expelled and carries with it silica and certain other mobile materials such as chlorine, fluorine, boron, sulphur, tellurium, etc., which are called mineralizers. The water also carries with it gold and other metals that are present in some magmas, dissolved with the help of the mineralizers. It is by means of the water from the magma that the metals are carried into the vein fissures.

Quartz is pure crystallized silica; it is not called quartz until it is deposited as we see it in the veins. The silica is transported upward in the vein fissure by the water in which it is dissolved, the solution of the quartz being aided by other substances in the water, especially by carbonic acid gas, which is the most abundant gas in magmas. The waters are at extremely high temperatures and pressures in the depths where they originate, so hot that they would explode into steam at atmospheric pressure. As the water flows upward into cooler rocks, both its temperature and its pressure decrease, and it is this decrease in temperature and pressure that causes the deposition of the quartz and metals and leaves the vein as we see it.

FIG. 1. Quartz vein outcropping near Indian Gulch, Mariposa County. Note the large crystal faces showing in the quartz to the left of the man. Some are more than four feet in length.

One point on which geologists do not agree concerns the sources of the water and silica. One school of thought believes that all the water and silica came from deep magmas, bringing with them the gold and other metals. A second school believes that most of the water by which the vein materials were carried in solution percolated into the fissures from the rocks of the surrounding country; and that the silica was dissolved from rocks adjacent to the fissure through the agency of carbonic acid gas that was contained in the solutions. Both theories are well reasoned and are based on close observations, and either is credible when read by itself.

Another point on which agreement has not been reached is the way in which the vein fissures have been opened wide enough to contain veins of the widths that are found in them. Open unfilled fissures do not and cannot exist in deep rocks. It is thought by some that the walls of the vein-fissures have been forced apart by a pressure and expansive force inherent in the vein-forming material itself, the force being due largely to the expansive force of compressed gases. By others it is thought that faulting, which is the slipping of one wall of a fissure over the other, caused the separation of the walls, each wall riding on the high spots of the other with a wedge-like effect; and that the open spaces were filled with quartz before they could be closed by a later movement. Movements of this kind, followed by cementation by quartz, if repeated over and over, could account for the widths in which the veins are found. Whatever is the true explanation, a stupendous force was required to push the walls apart.

Perhaps these problems will never be fully cleared up because the true explanations depend so much on facts and conditions that are only partly known, and on processes that are arrived at only by deduction. The case is somewhat similar to that known in criminal law as one of circumstantial evidence, a verdict being convincing as far as sufficient, reliable evidence is available. But for general information this much can be said with confidence, and this is my answer to the opening question: The veins were deposited in deep fissures, far below what was then the surface of the earth, from hot, ascending, water solutions containing silica and other mineral substances; that these substances remained in the solution while it was hot and under high pressure; and that the quartz and gold was deposited in the higher parts of the fissures because of a lowering in both temperature and pressure.

FIG. 2. Mother Lode quartz vein outcropping in a long vertical reef running from left to right across the background of the picture. Such reefs are to be seen on many parts of the Mother Lode. The above outcrop is close to Highway 49 near Coulterville.

FIG. 3. "White Rock"—a quartz vein outcropping in the vicinity of Indian Gulch, Mariposa County.

MINING ON CARSON HILL

By John A. Burgess

News of the gold discovery at Coloma spread fast. Jim Carson heard it at Monterey. Carson, a veteran of the then recent Mexican war, quickly assembled a group of fellow veterans and set out for the mountains. His party reached Carson Creek, in what is now Calaveras County, in August 1848. They dug in the gravel of the creek, they panned, they lived on beans, and then Jim Carson wrote a letter. He reported that, as a result of the first six day's work, they had taken out 186 ounces of gold apiece. He said they were "the happiest men on earth." Just how long Jim Carson dug and panned and ate beans is not told but apparently he made a satisfactory stake and returned home. And then, in 1853, he wrote another letter, this time to his old friends in the California diggings:

"It is to you, diggers, I speak—you who are enduring the hardships of the mountains, and working hard to honestly gain a fortune. Many of you, no doubt, are not making much more than what supports you comfortably, but a majority of you are getting more money per day for your labor than you could earn per week at any place in the civilized world; and you are happy, independent, and your own masters. A great many are realizing fortunes in a short time. Don't any of you despair; there are just as rich diggings as ever have been discovered and as large 'chunks' beneath the earth yet as have ever been taken therefrom. It is true you have to work harder now to get it than formerly, yet it is to be had . . . Never give up or think that the days of making fortunes in the gold mines have passed. Thousands will be making fortunes in California a hundred years hence."

Jim Carson had turned prophet. His "hundred years hence" is almost here today, and thousands are making fortunes in California; not, as Jim thought, in mining gold—for gold mining today is in a barren zone—but in hundreds of other occupations. We can credit Jim Carson with 100 percent efficiency as a gold digger and 99 percent as a prophet.

The gold in Carson Creek was getting scarcer. John Hance began to use his head and wondered where the placer gold came from. Streaks of gold in the wash at the side of the creek were pointing up the hill. John Hance saw the great white outcrop of bull quartz on Carson Hill and decided to investigate it. A little digging, a little panning, more eating of beans, and John Hance found rich gold ore in the outcrops just west of the big vein. He then formed a partnership and began mining in solid ground. Nearly $3,000,000 in gold is reported to have been taken out in less than the next two years. The notorious scoundrel, Billy Mulligan and his gang, took forcible possession of the place but after holding it for nine months they were ejected by court order in 1853. In 1854, a lump of gold was mined that weighed 2340 troy ounces (160 lb. avoirdupois), valued at $43,534.

The hill was covered with mining locations. The site of Hance's discovery where the richest ore was found was included in the Morgan claim, which finally came into the possession of a young miner named James G. Fair, and the title continued with Fair and his heirs until 1918. Fair sank a shaft west of the Bull vein and it is said that the gold he took out formed the beginning of his immense fortune. The last of his old mine workings were blasted out in the excavation of the footwall gloryhole in 1935, by the Carson Hill Gold Mining Co. under the direction of the writer.

After the rich ores near the surface had been exhausted mining operations were few and small until about 1898. During this period highgraders worked surreptitiously in the Morgan mines reportedly with good results for themselves; Dona Elisa Martinez (tradition says she was beautiful, and maybe she was) operated a lease profitably on the South Carolina mine; the Stanislaus mine at Melones took out a good body of highgrade ore at Melones—it was at this mine that calaverite, a gold telluride, and melonite, a nickel telluride, were first found and identified; the "Old English Company" operated a mill on the Calaveras mine; two newly arrived boys from Missouri asked at the English mine how to put in a blast, and then proceeded to practice their new accomplishment in a place that took their amateur fancy, and scattered gold all over the hillside.

There are two principal veins on Carson Hill. The Bull vein, the most easterly, is the one exposed in the glory holes high on the mountain, visible from the highway from north of the town of Carson Hill; and the Calaveras vein, the main representative of the Mother Lode in this locality, is the one seen in excavations west of the highway on the Melones side of the hill. The Bull vein—the name is used here to cover both the wide vein of barren bull quartz and the gold bearing quartz and schist along its borders—is the one from which most of the production was made. The early bonanza diggings and the later operations of the big companies were on this vein system. The gold bearing outcrop has now been mined out. Its extent of about 1300 feet is now marked by the Melones gloryhole, farthest to the south; and by the Footwall gloryhole and the Union pit, separated by the bull quartz vein, on the north.

Mining on a large scale was started in 1898, when the Melones Mining Co., headed by Mr. W. B. Devereaux of New York, began work on the lowgrade ore at the surface along the east side of the Bull vein, south of the Morgan claim. The ore carried $2 to $3 in gold. It was milled in a 100-stamp mill and cyanide plant at Melones. It was this company that drove the 4500-foot tunnel from Melones to beneath the ore bodies at Carson Hill, and sunk the Melones shaft to the 3000-foot level. The operation was well planned and well managed. Mining and milling costs were low; for 1908-10 they were $1.08 per ton. After adding the loss of gold in tailing, anything in excess of the combined figure was operating profit. By 1914 the cost had risen to $1.60 per ton, and by 1918 still farther rising costs and the low grade of the ore forced the closing of the mine. It had produced about $4,000,000.

At one stage in this operation affairs had reached a crisis. The manager reported to the home office in New York that in order to continue operations a big new hoist must be purchased and a deeper shaft sunk. Twenty-five thousand dollars was required for the purpose, and it was questionable whether the money would be forthcoming. Then, before a reply could be received, came one of those astounding turns of fortune of which a gold mine is capable. A raise on the 1350-foot level, being driven for an orepass, encountered a rich pocket of specimen ore in the footwall of the Bull vein that produced the $25,000 almost overnight. A quick telegram relieved the pressure on the New York office.

In 1920, The Carson Hill Gold Mines, Incorporated, with Mr. W. J. Loring as manager, consolidated all the old mines on Carson Hill between the villages of Carson Hill and Melones, and took over the property of the Melones mine. This company found a rich oreshoot on the Morgan claim and mined it down to a depth of 4550 feet. Cut samples showed as high as $80 per ton and mill heads assayed over $20 per ton at times, but the average grade of the oreshoot was $12.60 per ton. Increasing costs and a lowering in grade of the ore closed the mine in 1926. The operation had produced about $6,000,000. The bottom of the mine when this company took it over was at 3000 feet. They left it at 4550 feet. The late Olaf Wenstrom, the last manager for the company, told the writer in a letter that there is still ore at the bottom, of good milling grade, some of it showing visible gold. No mining has been done since at that depth.

After a shutdown of seven years, a new operation of the mine was undertaken by the Carson Hill Gold Mining Company with the writer in charge. Work was started in April 1933. It was planned to work the marginal ores of $2 to $3 grade. Wages and the costs of materials were low and much of the necessary equipment was on the property. The cost of repairs to equipment and mine workings was correctly estimated at $100,000.

The times then were hard. Men were out of work. Miners were eking out an existence on ranches, in pocket mining, and in placering the already worked gravels. One man, a graduate engineer, told the writer he was getting 85 cents a day from his pocket mining, and others told a similar story. Miners were back again to pork and beans, with little pork. It was a time for gold mining to get busy.

Mining was begun where ore could be produced at the least cost. The footwall gloryhole was worked and excavation of the Union pit by power shovel was started. The ore from these workings was dropped through an ore pass to loading chutes in the long haulage tunnel. Two shovel pits were operated on the outcrop of the Calaveras vein, from which the ore was hauled by trucks to loading chutes. Underground mining also was done on upper levels of the Morgan and Calaveras mines. Early in the operation the price of gold was increased from its traditional price of $20.67 per ounce to $35 per ounce, and this made ore of lower gold content profitable to work. Underground mining then progressed to greater depth until it was at the 3500-foot level.

The mill, at the start, had a capacity of 650 tons per day, but this was later increased to a maximum of 1100 tons per day. Gold recovery was by amalgamation, concentration, and cyaniding. All gold was turned out in the form of bullion bars and no concentrate was shipped. The huge tailing pile at Melones, over 3,000,000 tons, represents all the ore produced by the Carson Hill Gold Mining Company and some from the preceding operation. Tailing from the Melones Company operation had been discharged into the river.

The Carson Hill Gold Mining Company continued operation until May 1942, when the stamp mill burned down. Any hope of rebuilding and resuming work was extinguished a few months later by government Order L-208, which required the closing of all gold mines as a war-time measure. Under this operation the mine produced 2,840,000 tons of ore from which $6,500,000 was recovered. It had paid for the purchase price of the mine and had paid eleven dividends.

There is no accurate record of the early production from Carson Hill but the total production is estimated to be over $26,000,000.

SURVEY OF BUILDING STRUCTURES OF THE SIERRAN GOLD BELT—1848-70

By Robert F. Heizer and Franklin Fenenga

INTRODUCTION

History

California, first seen by Caucasians almost exactly 50 years after the discovery of America, lived for three hundred years as a distant and neglected outpost of Spain and her satellite, Mexico. Of all the historic events in which California has participated, none has so stirred the imagination or achieved such significance as the discovery of gold by James Wilson Marshall at Coloma on January 24, 1848, and the Gold Rush of 'forty-nine and the 'fifties. In the century since the gold discovery, California has achieved a population in excess of 10 million, and many of its citizens are descendants of the early argonauts; but the days of the Gold Rush are over, and the gold region has turned to other things. Nature had mined and milled the gold-bearing rocks in her rivers for millions of years, and after the golden harvest had been reaped from the recent stream bottoms and exposed Tertiary gravel deposits, the great Gold Rush was over. Underground mining began only 18 months after Marshall's discovery, and continues today, but the number of worked out and abandoned mines far exceeds those in present operation. Hydraulic placer mining went into decline in 1884 and ceased, for all practical purposes, with the Caminetti act of 1893. Although the word gold is automatically associated with the Mother Lode, this is true largely in a historic sense—the present day is one of different economic interests and exploitation. Lumbering, building stone quarrying, cement kilns, the tourist trade, and farming have replaced gold extraction as a means of livelihood. Of over five hundred towns which developed in the gold region between 1848 and 1860, more than 50 percent have disappeared from the present day maps. Of the other half, most exist as place names, and only a small portion are thriving communities at present. Survival has been possible only through developing local resources other than gold.

Object of the Survey

The present study concerns the permanent buildings of stone and clay built in the gold mining region in the two decades following the gold discovery. These buildings are the enduring monuments raised by the men who came in answer to the call of gold. Each year sees more of them destroyed through neglect or intent, and it was in the hope of recording certain essential information on the condition and construction of the accessible remaining structures that this survey was undertaken. Our project is potentially valuable in economic terms. The bricks molded of local clays all the way from Mariposa to North San Juan have withstood a near-century of foothill weather, surely a strong recommendation for the quality of the brick earths of the region. In western Amador and El Dorado Counties the abundant rhyolite tuff, used locally for building stone as early as 1851, has withstood the test of time with distinction. Labor costs and disinterest in erecting hewn stone buildings have contributed to the abandonment of the tuff quarries, but they remain today as potential sources of easily worked and attractive structural stone.

Acknowledgments

Throughout the course of our study we have been aided by advice and technical information from Dr. Olaf P. Jenkins, Chief, State Division of Mines. His thorough acquaintance with the Sierran Gold Belt geology, towns, history, and people has proved invaluable to us. Mr. Oliver Bowen, State Division of Mines, accompanied us over most of the area surveyed, and his pleasant companionship and technical advice on geological matters were of very great aid. Everywhere we found the local residents anxious to assist us in identifying old stone buildings. As a result of the persistent questioning to which they cheerfully submitted, we secured information on a number of buildings which were hitherto unrecorded or incorrectly described in the historical literature. We enjoyed and appreciate the opportunity to have become acquainted with the people of the Gold Rush country because they are interested in their heritage and were willing to accept outsiders who professed a similar interest. Dr. Aubrey Neasham of the National Park Service, with whom both present authors collaborated in the 1947 excavation of the Sutter Sawmill, made available to us the manuscript file and photographs of the Historic American Building Survey. In the photographs shown here some are identified as HABS (Historic American Building Survey), and the appended number is the negative number in the HABS file. Credit for each picture so listed is hereby acknowledged to Dr. Neasham, the National Park Service, and the Historic American Building Survey. The symbol DMBS refers to the reconnaissance reported in this paper and known as the Division of Mines Building Survey. The number following the survey initials refers to the negative number. All film negatives of DMBS pictures used in the present report are on file in the library of the State Division of Mines, Ferry Building, San Francisco. A large number of printed books have been consulted in the effort to determine the names of builders and dates of erection of the stone structures described below. On the last page of this report we list those printed works which may be of particular interest to the Mother Lode traveler.

UTILIZATION OF FIREPROOF BUILDING MATERIALS

The stone, brick, and adobe architecture of the Mother Lode region arose chiefly in response to the danger and the disaster of fire. The first settlements of the gold seekers were unplanned congested hodgepodges of canvas and frame shelters. Open flame fires were necessary for heat, cooking, and illumination and even a minor accident could initiate a conflagration. A fire, once started, could scarcely ever be checked and the devastation of entire towns occurred time after time. An incomplete list reveals that Sonora was burned in 1849, in 1852, and in 1853; Nevada City in 1851, 1856, 1858 and 1863; San Andreas in 1856 and 1863; and Columbia was partially destroyed by fire in 1854, 1857 and 1861. Disastrous fires also are reported for Grass Valley in 1855, Downieville in 1852, Placerville in 1856, Mokelumne Hill in 1854, Drytown in 1857, Jamestown in 1855, Georgetown in 1852, and Calaveritas and Campo Seco in 1858.

The miners strove to protect their property in various ways. Every town had its volunteer fire department and some of the larger towns had several fire companies. Elaborate fire fighting equipment was imported (some of the hoses were to serve later in the first hydraulic mining enterprises) and streets were required by ordinance to be wide enough to serve as fire lanes. But the primary danger still lay in the combustibility of building materials and the answer was found in the exploitation of architectural materials which are seldom used in other regions where ample stands of good timber are immediately at hand. Buildings designed for permanence were constructed of stone or brick or occasionally of adobe. Heavy raftered roofs were covered with metal and on top of this a thick layer of sand was deposited. Doors and windows were fitted with the distinctive sheet-iron shutters designed so that they could be closed in an emergency to protect the combustible interior furnishings. These efforts were on the whole successful, as indicated by the number of such buildings which have survived the various conflagrations.

The necessity for fireproof construction was not the only feature which determined the choice of architectural materials. The varied cultural background of the argonauts was a factor here as well as in styles. Many of the miners from Mexico as well as those Californians who had already been here for a generation were accustomed to building with adobe, sun-dried mud blocks several times larger than conventional bricks. These were laid flat, usually without mortar. Adobe buildings are seen most frequently in the centers of Mexican activity (Hornitos and Sonora) but this material was adopted by others. The frugal Chinese, who gleaned from the abandoned workings of other peoples, especially appreciated this most economical building material. Brick was the favored building medium of the Americans. It symbolized for them substance and permanence and its prestige is reflected in the widespread use of brick façades for stone buildings. Some stone structures were also built by Americans for New Englanders. Middlewesterners were accustomed to building dry rock walls with stone cleared from fields; to building frame structures on stone foundations; and to lining cellar walls with mortar-laid stone. The stone masons par excellence were the Italians who came to the gold fields. In the central and southern section of the Mother Lode region a large proportion of the good stone buildings, especially those of rhyolite tuff, bear Italian names.

Fig. 1.   Wall of old print shop at Mokelumne Hill showing details of hand-chipped blocks of rhyolite tuff.

The large number of ruins of stone, brick and adobe buildings may be partly accounted for by the fact that the Sierra lies outside the earthquake region. If this area were subject to earth tremors the number of standing walls would surely be much reduced.

Rhyolite tuff, known locally as "lava" is one of the few stone materials which was quarried and transported beyond its local occurrence for use as a building material. The reasons for its popularity can easily be recognized. It is as durable as any material which was available in the Gold Rush days but more important, is soft enough that it can easily be dressed with the stone mason's adze. This workability permits the cutting of long narrow blocks to serve as lintels over doors and windows; the dressing of all six faces of a block so that it can be squarely fitted with a minimum of mortar; the dressing of thin blocks for facing over a rubble core; and the use of the keystone. There are old rhyolite tuff quarries near Fiddletown, Altaville and Mokelumne Hill and the high knoll which provided Altaville with its first building stone is still being quarried.

Wherever it is immediately available, rhyolite tuff is used in the construction of all four walls of buildings and occasionally for such ordinary purposes as stone retaining-walls and fences. Beyond the limits of its natural occurrence, it has been transported to such towns as Murphys, San Andreas, Placerville, and Coloma, where it is employed to construct decorative façades for buildings the other walls of which are made of various local field rocks.

A very similar stone as far as gross appearance and quality of workability are concerned is tuffaceous sandstone derived from the Valley Springs formation. There is an old quarry of tuffaceous sandstone at Littlehales and buildings made from it are there and at Jenny Lind. Several buildings in Campo Seco utilize tuffaceous sandstone for an ornamental façade.

Meta-andesite agglomerates, commonly called greenstones, occur in a band of varying width along the entire western border of the Mother Lode. In the immediate locale of its occurrence meta-andesite is employed for most building purposes. Unlike the schists, it has no well defined planes of cleavage, and unlike rhyolite tuff and sandstone, it is too hard to be easily squared and dressed. In consequence these irregular blocks cannot be set in a wall without the use of heavy mortar, such as mud, which was occasionally used, or lime, which was commonly used. Greenstone was seldom obtained from special quarries and it appears that surface fieldstone (float) was the usual source. When it is used as a structural material in towns, the building façades are of materials regarded as more ornamental, such as brick or rhyolite tuff.

Schists of the Calaveras, Cosumnes, and Mariposa series as well as some similar formations of earlier age are extensively used as building material. Their especial virtue lies in the fact that they usually have well defined horizontal planes of cleavage which permit the detachment of large, even surfaced slabs which can be used with very little dressing or shaping (cf. Figs. 13, 26). When used for fences or retaining walls, they are often dry-laid (cf. Figs. 25, 168), but in buildings they are usually set in mortar of mud or lime. When the vertical plane of cleavage is definite, it is set toward the exterior. The rough, vari-colored appearance of schist walls was not always appreciated by the early builders and most schist buildings have façades of brick (Fig. 42) or of dressed blocks of ornamental stone (mostly rhyolite tuff) and the other walls are heavily coated with lime stucco. That the use of schist as a structural material is confined to those towns where it is available in the immediate locale, indicates that it was employed because of convenience rather than preference. Representative schist buildings are illustrated in Figs. 12, 33, 46, 126.

Granite, superb building material that it is, is seldom used in construction in the Mother Lode. Perhaps it was regarded as a too pretentious material for the essentially functional architecture of the mining camps. San Francisco's first fireproof building the three-story Parrott Block, was made of granite. It was "pre-fabricated," the blocks were cut and fitted in China, marked with Chinese characters, and shipped to California to be erected by Chinese labor in 1852. Local granite, quarried at Quincy, was advertised for sale in San Francisco, by Coit and Beals at the Sign of the Granite Obelisk, 94 Battery St. in a Jan. 1, 1854 advertisement in the *Alta California*. The granite quarries at Folsom were opened in 1856 and operated by convict labor. The Penryn granite quarry was opened by G. Griffith in 1864.

Rough quarried granite blocks used in early structures may be seen at the old winery two miles east of Rescue (Fig. 130), at Lotus, and at several places on Highway 49 between Lotus and Pilot Hill. Dressed granite blocks are to be seen in Mariposa, the source being Mormon Bar immediately to the south, and at Coloma (Fig. 133).

Serpentine resembles meta-andesite agglomerate as far as its qualities as a building material are concerned. Field stones of serpentine of irregular sizes and shapes were occasionally used for structural purposes in the immediate locale of their natural occurrence but no intensively worked quarries were seen nor was there any evidence that the serpentine was transported more than few hundred yards.

Talc schist, or soapstone as it is called in the Mother Lode, was occasionally employed in its rough form in rubble walls of buildings (for example the Butterfly Grocery in Mariposa) or in carefully sawed blocks used as an ornamental facing material as it is in the Coulter Hotel in Coulterville and the window arches of the Cory Building in Auburn (Fig. 130). It is surprising that a stone which is so easily worked and so resistant to heat and weathering was not used more extensively.

Limestone (including marble) is of very local occurrence, good exposures being noted at Columbia, Murphys, Volcano, and Cool. Limestone buildings can be seen in Douglas Flat and in Murphys and the buildings in Volcano are almost completely constructed of this material. Curiously, the limestone seems never to have been used for structural purposes in the vicinity of Columbia although some fine marble was quarried here in 1852 and shipped to San Francisco. E. R. Roberts of Stockton established a marble yard at Columbia in 1857, and in that year a block of Columbia marble was sent to the national capital to be put in the Washington Monument. In 1852 a block of marble from the Ringgold quarry measuring 48 by 22 by 22 inches and weighing 2700 pounds was cut for the Washington Monument, but whether it arrived does not appear to be recorded in the account printed in the *Alta Californian*, Dec. 3, 1852. The stone for the Broderick Monument in San Francisco came from the Columbia quarry.

One of the most important structural materials in use in the Mother Lode region was brick. It was used throughout the area in the chimneys and fireplaces of wooden buildings, and to frame the doorways and

FIG. 2. Commemorative plaque on Telephone Building at French Corral, Nevada County.

windows of buildings whose walls were of rough stone. A few towns, located where good brickmaking lateritic clays were available, were the centers of the brick industry. In particular, Columbia, Grass Valley, ·Georgetown, and North San Juan are noteworthy as places in which brick is virtually the only fireproof building material employed.

The first brickmaking in upper California was done in 1847 at the kiln of G. Zins established at Sutterville, just south of Sacramento. In 1847 Zins burned 40,000 bricks, and in 1848 his yard produced 100,000. It seems probable that some of the earliest brick buildings in the Mother Lode were made of Zins brick. Bekeart's store in Coloma, built in 1853, was made of Sacramento brick. J. Doak had a brickyard at Stockton in 1850, and in that year turned out 700,000 bricks, some of which were sold in San Andreas and Coulterville. The local supply, however, did not meet the demand, for in 1849 a shipload of brick from Plymouth, Massachusetts, sold in San Francisco for $60 a thousand, and in 1851 an editorial complaint in the *Daily Alta Californian* warned its readers of the dangers of fire, bemoaned the expense of imported brick, and commented that California brick, when available, brings from $36 to $80 a thousand, but "has no good glaize." The disastrous fires throughout the Mother Lode and the brick building boom of the 'fifties forced an expansion of the industry. Placerville and Shaws Flat had brickyards in 1853. An advertisement by Stout and Wall, contract builders, in the Columbia *Argus* in 1854 offered brick at the kiln for $8 per thousand, $10 delivered, and $20 per thousand laid in the walls. By 1856 the Sutterville kilns were selling brick for $7 per thousand at the kiln and $8 delivered. In 1858 the Sacramento brickyards produced 1,500,000 bricks for the San Francisco harbor defenses. In 1854, two years after the great fire in Sacramento, the city had over 500 brick houses. Less than a year after the Nevada City fire of 1856, 25 fireproof brick structures had been erected. These examples illustrate the trend toward fireproof construction at the height of the Gold Rush.

Brick never became cheap enough to use for retaining walls, corrals, or farm fences. It appears always to have been a structural material which carried considerable prestige, since it was used for the façades of stone structures in many towns. The stucco covering of stone and adobe buildings was frequently grooved and painted to simulate brick (cf. Fig. 30). Building in stone and brick gave rise to one quarrying activity, for brick must be set in lime mortar. Early lime kilns in which limestone was burned were situated at Shaws Flat, Ione, and Cool. Most of the stone buildings seen on our survey were built with mud mortar, or a mixture of mud and lime. Lime must have been scarce and expensive, and when available was used to plaster the outside and interior walls of rough stone or adobe buildings. Information on the early utilization of concrete is difficult to obtain. Columbia had, in 1855, a brick reservoir lined with cement, and in 1856 Columbia had a building which was then unusual, if not unique for the Mother Lode, made of aggregate (concrete and gravel). It was destroyed in the 'sixties in order to mine the gravels on which it stood. In Coulterville a large concrete foundation may be seen which is surely very old, but we were unable to obtain information on when it was built.

Adobe construction was first introduced to California from Mexico by the Spanish in the late eighteenth century during the Mission period. It was in general use throughout the occupied areas of California at the time of the gold discovery in 1848, and the impulse to build with adobe bricks in the Mother Lode almost certainly derives from Americans and Mexicans living in California before 1848, who went to the gold regions of the Sierra. Adobe buildings are of two fundamental forms; those with walls of sun-dried bricks laid up dry or with mud mortar (cf. Figs. 14, 80), and those with walls formed by ramming or pounding stiff earth or clay between molds similar to the molds we now use for pouring concrete. Both methods are common in Spanish countries, and the latter is referred to as *pisé* or *tapia*. Only three examples of the pisé technique were noted by us; two at Virginiatown (Fig. 152), and one at Fiddletown (Fig. 114). Adobe brick structures occur at Mormon Bar, Mt. Bullion, Bear Valley, Hornitos, near Bagby, Coulterville, Quartzburg, Sonora, Knights Ferry, San Andreas, Calaveritas, Jenny Lind, La Grange, Drytown, Fiddletown, and Mokelumne Hill. Others are reported from Salt Springs Valley, Old Gulch, and Mountain Ranch (Calaveras Co.), Shawmut and Jamestown (Tuolumne Co.), Dutch Flat (Placer Co.), and Frenchtown (Yuba Co.). In general, adobe buildings occur frequently along the western margin of the gold belt, and are most concentrated in the south. Less rainfall along the low-altitude western foothills may have encouraged mud-brick architecture, and in the south the greater Mexican-Spanish influence was doubtless largely responsible for the large numbers of adobe structures. Adobe buildings are often ascribed to Chinese builders, but it would be incorrect to so attribute all such structures. The Chinese were frugal people, and lumber and brick were expensive. The lateritic clays of the western Sierra slopes bind well, and offered an inexpensive and relatively durable building material. Therefore, adobe buildings may reflect, as for example at Hornitos, either a common pre-1848 Californian architectural technique which was practiced by Mexicans through traditional preference, or they may have been built by underprivileged minority groups such as the Chinese for reasons of economy because they were cheap and easy to erect.

The usual practice was to coat the exterior walls with a lime plaster about one-half inch thick. This was then whitewashed. So long as the overhanging eaves and roof kept in good condition, the plastered adobe

FIG. 3.   Fremont Co. Office, Mariposa, HABS 1528.

FIG. 5.   Trabucco Warehouse, Mariposa, DMBS Mrp-H2.

FIG. 4.   Schlageter Hotel, Mariposa, DMBS Mrp-H1.

FIG. 6.   Chinese adobe buildings, HABS 1529.

would last indefinitely, but access to the walls by rain water would cause their rapid dissolution, since the bricks were composed only of sun-dried earth. In one instance (the Bruschi Warehouse in Coulterville), the large adobe bricks were fired.

MARIPOSA

The town of Mariposa marks the southern end of the Mother Lode and Highway 49. It is also located on Highway 140, about halfway between Merced and Yosemite Valley. In 1844 Micheltorena, then Mexican Governor of California, granted to Juan Bautista Alvarado the land which in 1847 was bought by John C. Frémont and later known as the Mariposa Grant. The first quartz mine in the Mother Lode was worked on the Frémont Grant in August 1849, only 18 months after James Marshall's discovery of gold at Coloma on the South Fork of the American River.

Mariposa retains abundant evidence of its growth in the 1850's and the visitor may see on the main street the old Frémont Company Office of brick, now much altered but still identifiable from the accompanying photograph (Fig. 3). Across the street is the old Schlageter Hotel (Fig. 4) built of brick and with wide wooden balconies. The Trabucco Warehouse of brick with its iron doors (Fig. 5), the present Bank of America Building and the I. O. O. F. Hall all evidence the early brick architectural styles of the 'fifties. Of the old stone buildings, the most accessible is the present Butterfly Grocery whose exposed inner walls are built of soapstone set in mud mortar. Source of the soapstone is the hillslopes immediately east of the town. The jail (Fig. 7) which sits on the hill at the southern end of town is made of dressed granite blocks from Mormon Bar two miles south of Mariposa. This granite is significant as it comes from the intrusion which terminates the Mother Lode on the south. No visitor in Mariposa should neglect seeing the wooden courthouse, erected in 1854, and built on classic lines.

MT. BULLION

The tiny rancher's village of Mt. Bullion, first settled in 1850, was the scene of intense mining activity and the site of the Princeton mine. On the east side of the highway are the remains of the Marre Store, made of adobe and built before 1860 (Fig. 8). The individual adobe bricks are 12 inches square and $3\frac{1}{2}$ inches thick.

HORNITOS

Hornitos, reached via side roads from Mt. Bullion and Bear Valley, was founded by Mexicans only a few months after Marshall's discovery of gold. The Spanish name (meaning "little ovens") derives, according to one report, from the domed stone and mud tombs whose remnants may still be seen on the hill just below the Catholic church. The visitor is immediately struck with the impression that here is a Mexican pueblo, as

FIG. 7.   Jail, Mariposa, DMBS Mrp-H3.

FIG. 8.   Marre adobe, Mt. Bullion, HABS 1527.

FIG. 9.   Plaza, Hornitos, HABS 1103.

FIG. 11.   D. Ghirardelli store, Hornitos, HABS.

FIG. 10.   Wells Fargo building, Hornitos, DMBS Mrp-H4.

FIG. 12.   Post Office (former dance hall), Hornitos, DMBS Mrp-H5.

indeed it is in origin and plan (Fig. 9). Few Mother Lode towns can match Hornitos for the number and charm of old buildings. Among the more interesting structures are the old Wells Fargo building (now the N. S. G. W. hall) with a brick front and quarried schist walls built in 1851 (Fig. 10), the Masonic Lodge (1860) of similar construction and with a limestone flagging which came from nearby rock exposures, the D. Ghirardelli store (1855) made of dressed schist with one adobe wall and an old brick building in back (Fig. 11), and the present Post Office built of dressed schist blocks (Fig. 12). This building was formerly a dance hall and saloon patronized by the notorious bandit, Joaquin Murietta, who used, in emergencies, an escape tunnel running from the dance hall under the road, with its exit in an adobe building. The tunnel measuring 2 by 3 feet and the remnants of the adobe "blind" may still be seen. The schist for the several stone-mud mortar buildings was quarried in the center of town (Fig. 13). Hornitos contains a number of adobe buildings (a feature emphasizing its Mexican aspect) whose preservation varies from complete structures to weathered remnants of walls. Figure 14 shows the adobe brick back wall of a store, built by Mexicans in 1851, which later became the Merck Bakery.

About three miles east of Hornitos on the road to Bear Valley is the site of Quartzburg. Here may be seen the remnants of the Thorne Store built in 1852 with adobe brick walls and a fired brick front.

MT. OPHIR

Now completely abandoned, Mt. Ophir is sometimes said to be the site of California's first mint. Although it is probably true that here were "coined" the famous octagonal fifty dollar gold slugs, the Pacific Company in San Francisco seems to have minted the first gold coins; these were stamped with the date 1849. Between 1849, when the Federal government authorized private coinage subject to approval by federal inspectors, and 1854 when the first United States Mint was opened in California, at least a dozen private coiners were at work. Of these Moffatt and Company was the largest. The foundations of the Mt. Ophir mint, about 30 feet square, may still be seen. Like the other ruins in Mt. Ophir, they are made of quarried slabs of schist set in mud mortar. The walls of a two room cabin (Fig. 15) are standing on the bank overlooking the mint foundation. The ruins of the Trabucco Store (Fig. 16) can be seen from the highway. It was built about 1853. The inner walls of this building are faced with a lime stucco. The local source of the building material can be seen in the open quarry drift on the east side of the highway (Fig. 17). Next to the road on the east are several stone house ruins (Fig. 18).

BEAR VALLEY

The little hamlet of Bear Valley, first named Simpsonville, is the site of a once important town in which John C. Frémont made his home. Several old stone buildings are still in use. All are made of schist slabs, set in lime mortar and plastered over with stucco. A detail of a

FIG. 13.   Schist quarry in Hornitos, DMBS Mrp-H6.

FIG. 14.   Wall of adobe building opposite Ghirardelli store, Hornitos, DMBS Mrp-H7.

Fig. 15. Two room cabin near Mt. Ophir mint, DMBS Mrp-H8.

Fig. 17. Schist quarry east of highway, Mt. Ophir, DMBS Mrp-H9.

Fig. 16. Trabucco store, Mt. Ophir, HABS 1524.

Fig. 18. Stone house ruin, Mt. Ophir, DMBS Mrp-H10.

FIG. 19.   Schist wall (detail), Bear Valley,
DMBS Mrp-H11.

FIG. 21.   Adobe building with stucco exterior,
Bear Valley, DMBS Mrp-H13.

FIG. 20.   Adobe building, Bear Valley, DMBS Mrp-H12.

FIG. 22.   Jail, Bear Valley, DMBS Mrp-H14.

weathered corner of the Frémont Company Store (now in ruins) is shown in Fig. 19. In one instance (a building on the west side of the highway at the south end of town) the stucco has been painted and grooved to resemble large, dressed blocks of stone. A local source for the stone building material is indicated by evidences of quarrying in schist outcrops within the town. The roofless stone jail stands on the hill near the schoolhouse (Fig. 22). Four adobe buildings also survive. One of these is unusual in having several courses of schist slabs laid in between courses of adobe blocks (Figs. 20, 21). At the northeast end of Bear Valley, the remains of its Chinatown can be seen in a row of clay hummocks and ruined fireplaces, the vestiges of the original adobe buildings.

BAGBY

Bagby is the site of Benton Mills, named by John C. Frémont for his father-in-law, Thomas Hart Benton. The foundations of the mill (Fig. 23) can be seen on the south bank of the Merced River just below the highway bridge and just above the mouth of Hell Hollow. Flat-laid slabs of serpentine set in lime mortar have been used in the construction. A mile downstream, on the south bank, is the site of the old Selby Ferry. A corral and a ruined adobe building still mark the site.

FRENCH MILLS

A mile and a half south of Coulterville and three-quarters of a mile west of Highway 49, are the ruins of the mine buildings and houses of the old site of French Mills. At present, the remains consist of a boiler house (Fig. 24), a series of retaining walls (Fig. 25), and several stone foundations, all constructed of schist slabs set in mud mortar and stucco covered. The source of this building material can be seen in the extensive quarrying of local outcrops (Fig. 26).

FIG. 23.   Foundations of Benton Mills, Bagby, DMBS Mrp-H15.

FIG. 25.   Schist retaining wall, French Mills, DMBS Mrp-H18.

FIG. 24.   Two views of boilerhouse (?), French Mills, DMBS Mrp-H16, H-17.

COULTERVILLE

Among the most interesting of the buildings in Coulterville are the ruins of a stone hotel. It is constructed of flat laid schist slabs (Fig. 28) but the front is covered with neatly dressed blocks of soapstone (Fig. 32). The soapstone facing blocks are said to have been quarried on the Gordon Place at Greely Mountain. Adjoining the ruins of the Coulter Hotel are the brick Wells Fargo office and Wagoner's store. Adjacent to this group is a schist quarry, the source of part of the building material. Across the highway (to the east) are several wells, lined with cobbles set in mortar and surmounted by a brick coping (Fig. 29). The Bruschi Building, once the alcalde's office, is of adobe with a plastered exterior grooved and painted to simulate fired brick (Fig. 30). The front half of the Bruschi Warehouse which now houses the fire department is made of schist slabs but its rear wing is made of *fired* adobe bricks each of which measures 15 by 7 by 4 inches. Several brick buildings may be seen as well as a few made of schist slabs. Fig. 31 shows the first Bruschi Store (left) of stone, and the second Bruschi Store (right) constructed of brick imported in the early 'fifties from Stockton. Most of the adobe buildings to be seen on the northern edge of Coulterville postdate 1870 but one, the Sun Sun Wo Store is said to date from 1851. One other building deserves mention; the ruins of a large, poured concrete foundation which may date from the Gold Rush period.

FIG. 26.   Schist quarry, French Mills, DMBS Mrp-H19.

FIG. 27.   Jail, Hornitos, HABS 1522.

FIG. 28.   Detail of schist wall, rear of hotel, Coulterville, DMBS Mrp-H20.

Fig. 29. Well on edge of highway, Coulterville, DMBS Mrp-H21.

Fig. 31. Brick and stone buildings, Coulterville, HABS 1532.

Fig. 30. Bruschi Building, Coulterville, HABS 1531.

Fig. 32. Hotel, Coulterville, DMBS Mrp-H22.

BIG OAK FLAT

Four miles east of Moccasin via Highway 120 is the town of Big Oak Flat, founded by James Savage in 1849. It is the site of one of the best preserved and most attractive stone buildings in the Mother Lode country. The Odd Fellows Hall is made of dressed schist slabs set in lime mortar. The door frames are made square by the use of brick (Fig. 33).

Nearby is Groveland, once named Garrote by the French miners. Here may be seen a splendid example of a brick front-schist walled building with its full complement of heavy iron doors and shutters.

CHINESE CAMP

Named for its Chinese laborers who settled here in 1849, Chinese Camp is famous in Gold Rush history. Most of its surviving buildings adhere closely to a single plan, side and rear walls are made of cobblestones (of gabbro and serpentine) set in mortar, and building faces are of brick. The ruins of the Wells Fargo Company Building, built in 1849, the Post Office (Fig. 34, left) and Rosenbloom's Store (Fig. 34, right) all are of this type. The ruins of one all-brick store can also be seen.

Among the ruins the "trees of heaven" *(Ailanthus)* have grown into a miniature forest. Wherever Chinese settled these trees were planted, and today their distribution along the Mother Lode attests the widespread presence of these people.

FIG. 33.   I. O. O. F. Hall, Big Oak Flat, HABS 1578.

FIG. 34.   Left: Post Office; right, store with iron doors, brick front, stone sides, Chinese Camp, DMBS Tuo-H1, H2.

FIG. 35.   Stone corral, Mountain Pass, DMBS, 233-B-11.

FIG. 36. House ruin, west of Mountain Pass, DMBS, 233-c-1.

FIG. 37. Tulloch Mill, Knights Ferry, HABS 1137-6.

MOUNTAIN PASS

Near the Mountain Pass School, on the south side of the road there is a stone corral made of dry-laid latite boulders (Fig. 35) derived from the lava cap Table Mountain which stands just north across the highway.

West of Mountain Pass on a knoll on the south side of the road, the ruins of a house, made of serpentine blocks set in lime mortar, can be seen (Fig. 36). The outcrop is nearby and shows signs of workings. Close by on the same knoll is another and similar stone ruin.

KNIGHTS FERRY

Settled by William Knight in 1848, this town on the Stanislaus River soon became a center for local mining and an important way point on the route to the Mother Lode. It is reached via Highway 120 and is located at the edge of the San Joaquin Valley east of Oakdale and west of Chinese Camp. Knight was succeeded by the Dent brothers (brothers-in-law to U. S. Grant), who built the Tullock Mill (Fig. 37) at the east end of town near the famous covered bridge. The brick one-story warehouse was raised in 1852-58 and the stone grist mill buildings were erected in 1862 by T. Vinson, an English stone mason. Vinson built the piers and abutments of the covered bridge in 1862-63. The brown and pink stone used in the Tullock Mill is local Ione sandstone quarried in the nearby slopes; other stones in the main east and south walls are from granite and conglomerate river boulders.

The use of local Ione sandstone is also evidenced in Knights Ferry in the low retaining walls (Fig. 40, left) which line the back streets and alleys. The famous iron jail is perhaps the most unusual one in the Mother Lode district. The Chinese are attributed authorship of the adobe brick houses, remnants of which may be seen south of the road near the jail. Their basement walls are of Ione sandstone blocks or rounded river cobble-mud mortar construction.

Fired brick was used for the old hotel which later became the courthouse. The basement excavation and remnants of the walls are all that are left of this building which was erected in 1859.

LA GRANGE

La Grange is located south of Highway 120 and west of Coulterville. Leaving Highway 120 and turning south, the motorist will see the low foothill elevations bordering the San Joaquin Valley. At Crimea House, 2.5 miles off Highway 120, is a circular stone corral on the east side of the road (Fig. 38). It was constructed in 1850 with Chinese labor of dry-laid schist blocks and measures about 80 feet in diameter with the walls over two feet thick and five feet high.

In La Grange proper is a beautifully preserved adobe brick building measuring 45 by 21 feet with walls 10.5 feet high and 18 inches thick.

FIG. 38.   Stone corral, Crimea House, DMBS Tuo-H3.

The mud bricks measure 10 by 17 by 4 inches. Its preservation is due to a wooden framing which is a later addition to the adobe which was built in the 'fifties. Opposite the adobe building is a pair of stone buildings complete with iron doors (Fig. 39). They are made of light tan-and-pink Ione sandstone which occurs just west of La Grange.

Two miles south of La Grange on the road to Coulterville is a stone-walled ditch used in earlier times for mining operations (Fig. 40, right). It is neatly made of dry-laid flat schist slabs gathered from the immediate vicinity.

JAMESTOWN

Jamestown, the historic "Jimtown," has a large number of stone buildings surviving from the Gold Rush period. These include the present Post Office which was formerly St. James Masonic Lodge, and other Main Street buildings. The construction of most buildings is masked by heavy coatings of stucco and false façades but the building pattern seems to have been consistently one of brick fronts with side and rear walls of schist slabs set in mortar in a manner similar to the buildings of Chinese Camp. Many years ago a Captain Neville built a hotel near the old depot whose lower walls were of green mariposite rock. It has since been destroyed and is mentioned here as the only instance encountered on this survey of the use of this rock in construction.

Midway between Jamestown and Sonora on the north side of the highway there is a house with a schist foundation and frame upper structure (Fig. 41).

FIG. 39.   Sandstone buildings, La Grange, DMBS, 233-D-4.

FIG. 40.   Left, sandstone wall, Knights Ferry, DMBS Sta-H1; right, stone-walled ditch, south of La Grange, DMBS Sta-H2.

SONORA

Sonora was named for the first gold seekers who settled here, Yaqui Indians from the State of Sonora in northwestern Mexico. It survives today as one of the largest and most vigorous towns of the Mother Lode country. It is an important center for lumbering as well as gold mining activity. Most of the evidences of the early town are concealed on the main streets by the practice of facing buildings with stucco, vitreous brick and other new materials but the same buildings viewed from side streets and alleyways reveal abundant evidence of early architecture.

As the visitor enters Sonora from Jamestown, a number of quarries in the schist bedrock can be seen along the right side of Highway 49. These are the sources of the town's favorite stone building material. Across the road to the west shoring and retaining walls made of dry-laid flat schist slabs channel the stream of Woods Creek.

The favored construction pattern in Sonora was that of making the sides and rears of buildings of flat laid schist slabs, the fronts of brick, but there are some all-brick buildings as well as some all-stone buildings and the influence of the Mexicans is to be seen in surviving adobes.

The building now known as the Opera Hall Garage was once the theater for Sonora. It still contains a stage and dressing rooms once used by the players. It has a brick front, and side and rear walls of schist slabs. The hillside behind the opera house was quarried to provide the building materials. At 919 Washington Street there is a two story building with a brick front and schist sides (Fig. 44). It was built in 1851 and is known as Rother's Tin Shop. Two adjacent buildings at 803 Stewart Street are of similar style but one is constructed of brick and the other of schist slabs with a brick front (Fig. 42). These were built by Americans and later sold to Chinese. Modern Sonorans refer to them as the "China Stores." At 905 Shepard Street there is a two story brick building resting on a foundation of schist slabs (Fig. 43). There is an all schist building opposite the Purity Store on Stewart Street (Fig. 46) and the old schist wall can be seen in the alleyway on the side of the Gem Cafe. Between the offices of the *Sonora Daily* and the police court, the ruins of the walls of an adobe building can be seen. The adobe blocks measure 13 by 6.5 by 3 inches. In 1850, Sonora had numerous adobe buildings including Captain Green's Hotel, a two story, 40 by 100 foot structure. The historic Italia Hotel, still in existence in Sonora (Fig. 45), contains at least one interior adobe wall of the original structure.

Fig. 41.   House with stone basement, between Sonora and Jamestown, DMBS Tuo-H4.

Fig. 42.   Building at 803 Stewart St., Sonora, DMBS Tuo-H5.

FIG. 43.   Home at 905 Shepard St., Sonora, DMBS Tuo-H6.

FIG. 44. Brick and schist building, 919 Washington St., Sonora DMBS Tuo-H7.

FIG. 45.   Italia Hotel, Sonora, SMBS Tuo-H8.

FIG. 46.   Schist building opposite Purity Store, Stewart St., Sonora, DMBS Tuo-H9.

Fig. 47. D. O. Mills building, Columbia, HABS 1573-2.

Fig. 48. Wells Fargo Express building, Columbia HABS 174-2.

COLUMBIA

The town of Columbia, once called "The Gem of the Southern Mines," is one of the architectural showplaces of the Mother Lode country. It was never abandoned; consequently the buildings never fell into complete disrepair; nor has it experienced the growth which led, in other towns, to false fronts and stucco covering. Almost all of its permanent buildings are made of brick, a reflection of the excellent brick-making lateritic clays available locally. Two brickyards (in operation in 1854) were located on the old Dambacher Ranch in Matelot Gulch, two miles north of Columbia. The extensive, marble-like, limestone outcrops seen in this region seem not to have been exploited for local building material although marble was quarried here and shipped to San Francisco as early as 1854.

Columbia's first brick building, completed in 1853, was torn down in 1866 and the bricks were sold in Sonora. Other brick buildings, were demolished in the 'sixties in order to mine the gravels under them, and the bricks resold in the nearby boom town of Copperopolis. Most of the historic buildings in Columbia are signed. Among them are the D. O. Mills Building erected in 1855 (Fig. 47), the Wells Fargo Express Office built in 1858 (Fig. 48), the Gold Nugget Saloon built in 1857, the Hildenbrand Building (now the N. S. G. W. Hall) erected 1855, the Levi Block built in 1854, and the Pioneer Saloon (Fig. 49), the Sun Tun Sing Company Building, St. Anne's Church, completed in 1856 (Fig. 50), the Masonic Hall built in 1854, the Odd Fellows Hall (Fig. 51) and the Springfield Brewery (Fig. 52). The cast iron grill work on the Express Building was made in New York.

Most of Columbia's brick structures postdate the great fire of 1854, which occurred only 4 years after the town was founded. Columbia, now a State Park, has numerous attractions in the form of exhibits of historical relics which the Mother Lode traveler may inspect.

Nine miles east of Columbia is French Camp, first settled by Frenchmen, where the Maisson Store, built in 1851 with lower walls made of schist, may be seen.

SHAWS FLAT

In the flat, lying between Sonora and Columbia, there were three Gold Rush settlements, Shaws Flat, Squabbletown, and Springfield. Among the interesting remnants to be seen in this area are the ruins of the two lime kilns (Fig. 53) which were used in the reduction of the local limestone to lime. These kilns date from 1852. The pitted limestone bedrock was extremely rich placer ground. The red lateritic earth was good for brick making, and some of the Sonora and Columbia bricks were molded and fired here in the early 'fifties.

At the site of the once populous town of Springfield is the well preserved remnant of a two story brick building, built in 1854, which has variously served as a church and an armory.

FIG. 49.   Pioneer Saloon, Columbia, HABS 1145-2.

FIG. 50.   St. Anne's Church, Columbia, HABS 1142-2.

Fig. 51.   I. O. O. F. Hall, Columbia, HABS 1720-2.

Fig. 52.   Springfield Brewery and Tuolumne Engine House No. 1 HABS 1711-1.

FIG. 53.   Lime kiln, Shaws Flat, DMBS Tuo-H10.

FIG. 54.   Left, Swerer's store, Tuttletown, DMBS 233-B-8.

FIG. 55. Stone house on Pendola ranch, Melones, DMBS Cal-H1

FIG. 56. Stone building, Carson Hill, DMBS Cal-H2.

TUTTLETOWN

The very well preserved and neatly built stone building which stands in Tuttletown was a store, built by W. Swerer in 1852, and patronized by Mark Twain during his sojourn at Jackass Hill. It is made of quarried and dressed blocks of Calaveras schist (Fig. 54). A schist quarry can be seen on the north side of the highway a half mile west of the store. Tuttletown was first settled by a group of Mormon prospectors in 1848 and then named Mormon Camp.

MELONES

The old town of Melones, at various times also called Roaring Camp and Slumgullion, lies on the north bank of the Stanislaus River. Melones was first settled by Mexican placer miners in 1848. To the east of the highway, several ruins of former schist buildings are to be seen including the Vignoli Gaming House built in 1850 and the homestead house on the Pendola Ranch (Fig. 55) about a mile northeast of town.

CARSON HILL

A few stone buildings made of flat Calaveras schist laid up with mud mortar (Fig. 56) may be seen. The famous Carson Hill mine, still in operation, is nearby, as is the site where the largest California gold nugget ever found was picked up in 1854. It weighed 195 pounds troy and would be worth roughly $73,710 at the present price of gold.

ALBANY FLAT

Between Carson Hill and Angels Camp near Frogtown in what was called Albany Flat stands the James Romaggi Fandango Dance Hall built in 1852 (Fig. 57). It has several rooms and is two stories high in the front. The walls are of selected coursed slabs of amphibolite schist. Few buildings in the entire Mother Lode can match this for size, excellence of construction, and elaborateness.

ANGELS CAMP

The modernized town of Angels Camp is built around a core of eighteen-fifty period stone structures. The Angels Hotel built in 1855 now bears a new façade, but is still recognizable in its earlier style shown in Fig. 56. It is built of dressed rhyolite tuff blocks, as are at least a dozen other buildings in town of equal age. Examples which show rhyolite block construction are the Stickle Store, Scribner's Store, the Wells Fargo Building and the present Sierra Club. Source of the tuff was the quarry east of Altaville (Fig. 63). A Chinese store built of brick is referred to locally as the "Chinese Calaboose."

FIG. 57.   Romaggi Fandango Hall, Albany Flat, DMBS Cal-H3.

FIG. 58.   Angels Hotel, Angels Camp, HABS 1547.

ALTAVILLE

Altaville, the historic Cherokee Flat (also known as Winterton and Forks of the Road), has one very well preserved stone building, the Prince and Garibardi Store, built in 1857 of dressed blocks of rhyolite tuff (Fig. 59). Several dryrock walls are built of the same material (Fig. 63) as is the Demarest Foundry. The North Branch Cemetery near Altaville contains several interesting tombstones, the legends of which suggest the rigour of life in the Gold Rush days (Figs. 60, 61, and 62). A mile east of Altaville on the road toward Murphys there is a prominent butte, capped with rhyolite tuff. Known locally as "lava" this material has been quarried since the 1850's and has provided a substantial, decorative building material for structures in Altaville, Angels Camp and Vallecito and facing and trim materials for buildings in more distant towns. This Peirano quarry is still in operation (Fig. 64).

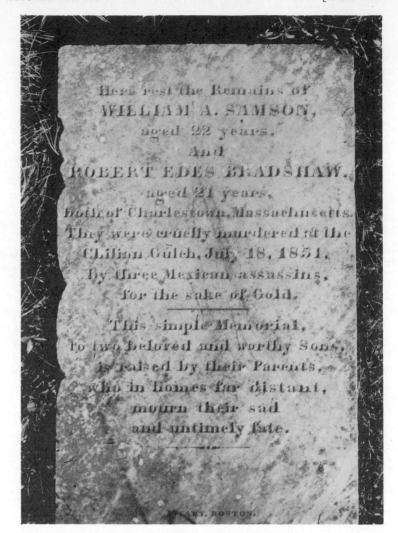

FIG. 60.   Gravestone, North Branch cemetery, near San Andreas. HABS, 1487-2.

FIG. 59.   Prince and Garabardi store, Altaville, HABS 1205-2.

FIG. 61.   Gravestone, North Branch cemetery, near
San Andreas, HABS, 1487-2.

FIG. 62.   Gravestone, North Branch cemetery, near
San Andreas, HABS, 1487-2.

FIG. 63.   Rhyolite tuff block fence just east of Altaville, DMBS Cal-H4.

FIG. 64.   Rhyolite tuff quarry, 1 mile east of Altaville, DMBS Cal-H5.

VALLECITO

Vallecito is on Highway 4, six miles from Angels Camp. Vallecito preserves the Wells Fargo Office, later Sanguinetti's and then Dinkelspiel's Store (Fig. 65) built in 1854. It is constructed of dressed blocks of rhyolite tuff which came from the Altaville quarry (Fig. 64). Across the road are the ruins of the Wells Fargo Stables put up in 1851 and made of the same material (Fig. 66), and up a side street is the splendid Cuneo building built in 1851 complete with iron doors and made of rhyolite tuff blocks (Fig. 67).

Beyond Vallecito at Douglas Flat, a distance of 2½ miles to the northeast, are a number of stone ruins which may be seen on either side of the road. The rough-quarried limestone here has served as a fence material. The Gilleado building built in 1851, now stabilized with concrete and with a new tin roof (Fig. 68), serves to illustrate the use of rough limestone blocks as a construction material in this vicinity and at Murphys not far beyond.

MURPHYS

Murphys, also located on Highway 4 to the northeast of Douglas Flat, is almost unique in preserving the atmosphere of a substantial Mother Lode town of the 'fifties (Fig. 69). Permanent buildings are of brick or quarried limestone. The Mitchler Hotel at Murphys (Fig. 70), made of rough quarried limestone chunks set in lime mortar, was built in 1855 by J. C. Sperry and J. Perry. It is supposed to be the one referred to in Bret Harte's "A Night in Wingdam." In the hotel register may be seen such names as Mark Twain, Thomas Lipton, Henry Ward Beecher, U. S. Grant, and J. J. Astor, Jr. Across the street is a typical Mother Lode brick-fronted, limestone rubble-lime mortar walled building which was in 1851 a miner's supply store and bakery. The simple charm of the St. Patrick's Catholic Church made of brick and dating from the 'fifties is a direct link with Murphys historic past (Fig. 71). The P. Travers building made of heavy limestone rubble and erected in 1856, is now Morley's Garage. It housed a store and the Wells Fargo Office. The Jones Apothecary shop (Fig. 72) with brick front and limestone rubble walls and Victorene Compere's Store (Fig. 73) with facing blocks of dark rhyolite tuff and walls of limestone rubble and now remodeled into an attractive private residence, complete our list here, but the visitor will identify many more structures which have come down to the present from nearly a hundred years ago. Less than a mile beyond Murphys on the road to Altaville there may be seen to the right several remnants of buildings made of schist slabs and rubble (Fig. 74).

FIG. 65.   Left, detail of rear wall, Wells Fargo Office, Vallecito; right, front door Wells Fargo Office, Vallecito, DMBS Cal-H6, H7.

FIG. 66.   Wells Fargo stables, Vallecito, DMBS Cal-H8.

FIG. 67.   Rhyolite tuff building, Vallecito, DMBS Cal-H9.

FIG. 68.   Limestone building, Douglas Flat, DMBS Cal.-H10.

Fig. 69.   Street view, Murphys, HABS 1211.

Fig. 70.   Mitchler Hotel, Murphys, HABS 1109-4.

Fig. 71.   St. Patrick's Church, Murphys, HABS 1112.

Fig. 72.   Jones Apothecary Shop, Murphys, DMBS Cal-H11.

Fig. 73. Victorene Compere's store, Murphys, HABS 1108-2.

FIG. 74.   Ruined schist-walled building just west of Murphys, DMBS Cal-H12.

FIG. 75.   Stone corral, 6 miles west of Altaville, DMBS Cal-H13.

COPPEROPOLIS

Six miles west of Altaville on the road to Copperopolis, two well preserved stone corrals can be seen (Fig. 75). They are made of serpentine and meta-andesite fieldstone.

Copperopolis is 12 miles west of Altaville via Highway 4. The mining of copper at this town began within a very few years after the gold discovery and its building boom shared the architectural styles of the Mother Lode country. Most of the standing buildings in Copperopolis are built of brick (some of which was secured from buildings which were torn down in Columbia in the 1860's) but there are some buildings and many foundations built of local fieldrock, mostly meta-andesite together with some schist and serpentine. Among the most interesting buildings to be seen is the Odd Fellows Hall, built as a church in 1862. It is built of brick and rests on a foundation of meta-andesite which contains copper ore. This foundation material is probably waste rock from one of the mines (Fig. 76). A store at the south end of town has a front section built of brick dovetailed into a rear section built of meta-andesitic field rock (Fig. 77).

SALT SPRINGS VALLEY

Salt Springs Valley, a few miles northwest of Copperopolis, was the site of several early-day mining and ranching ventures. Scattered stone and adobe buildings of the 'fifties occur in this valley, particularly on the Andrew Williams ranch where there was once a town called Felix or Stone Creek Settlement (Fig. 78).

JENNY LIND

Jenny Lind, today almost deserted, was a booming town during the Gold Rush and vestiges of her previous opulence are seen in the abandoned ruins of stone and adobe buildings. The town can be reached from Copperopolis via Salt Springs Valley and Milton. It is seven miles north of Milton. A building made of carefully dressed blocks of tuffaceous sandstone (Fig. 79) was once a grocery store. The building material was quarried near Valley Springs, a few miles to the north. One large adobe structure still stands (Fig. 80). Its foundation is made of local fieldstone. An old quarry, dug into an outcrop of Ione silty sandstone can be seen on the hillside just behind the town (Fig. 81).

FIG. 76.   I. O. O. F. Hall, Copperopolis, DMBS Cal-H14.

FIG. 78.   Mine building, Salt Springs Valley, HABS.

FIG. 77.   Brick and schist building, Copperopolis DMBS Cal-H15.

FIG. 79.   Tuffaceous sandstone building, Jenny Lind, DMBS Cal-H16.

CAMPO SECO

Three miles north of Valley Springs, which is on Highway 8 west of San Andreas, is Campo Seco, scene of the historic legal dispute over the Campo Seco Land Grant. The most interesting buildings in this town are the two story buildings of the Adams Express Company and the smaller buildings adjacent to it (Fig. 82). The fronts of each of these structures is made of carefully dressed blocks of tufaceous sandstone, the sides and rear walls of rough hewn fieldstones of meta-andesitic agglomerate. Just west of this row of buildings the brick oven of an old bakery can be seen (Fig. 83).

DOGTOWN

A quarter of a mile north of Altaville on Highway 49 is the Calaveritas road which turns off to the right. Dogtown, which lay on the edge of the flat at San Domingo Creek, is marked on the right side of the road by a stone fireplace and on the left by a large house ruin of schist set in mud mortar (Fig. 84).

Calaveritas, about five miles northwest of Dogtown, contains a number of adobe brick buildings erected in 1850 and 1851. Fig. 85 is a photograph of a somewhat dilapidated, but still well preserved structure, built in 1850. The exterior still bears the original lime plaster which served to protect the mud bricks from disintegration. The bricks measure 13 by 7.5 inches and are 5 inches thick. Just beside this adobe are the remnants of two other buildings whose basement walls, four feet high, are composed of schist, and quartzite rubble and fieldstone laid up in mud mortar with adobe walls on top. Each has an arched doorway in the stone basement wall, which faces to the south. Originally one of these was partially faced with well dressed granite blocks. Just beyond and around the bend is the Costa and Palmer adobe-brick store erected in 1851. The present owner has kept it in nearly perfect condition. Behind, in the farmyard, is a second adobe building, originally a house, which has schist rubble foundation walls. Still a third remnant like the last lies just to the west of the store across a small creek.

FIG. 80.   Adobe building, Jenny Lind, DMBS Cal-H17.

FIG. 81.   Ione silt-sandstone quarry, Jenny Lind DMBS Cal-H18.

Fig. 82.   Adams Express Co. building, Campo Seco DMBS Cal-H19.

Fig. 84.   House ruin, Dogtown, DMBS Cal-H21.

Fig. 83.   Brick and stone oven, Campo Seco DMBS Cal-H20.

Fig. 85.   Adobe brick house, Calaveritas, DMBS Cal-H22.

FIG. 86.   I. O. O. F. Hall, San Andreas, DMBS Cal-H23.

FIG. 87.   Superior Garage, San Andreas, DMBS Cal-H24.

FIG. 88.   J. Banque store, San Andreas, DMBS Cal-H25.

FIG. 89.   Friedburger Building (no longer standing) San Andreas, HABS 1478.

SAN ANDREAS

The main street of San Andreas displays several buildings dating from the 'fifties. Among these are the I. O. O. F. Hall made of brick and erected in 1856 (Fig. 86), the Corcoran and Sullivan building constructed of dressed granite blocks in 1855 (Fig. 87), and the J. Banque Store on Court Street with granitic walls and a brick front built in 1851 (Fig. 88) and said to be the oldest brick building in this section of the Mother Lode district. The adobe brick buildings adjoining the Banque Store date from the early 'seventies. The Friedburger building, otherwise known as the Calaveras Bar, has now been torn down but an earlier photograph is reproduced here (Fig. 89) to illustrate a common architectural technique of applying a smooth stucco outside over the stone walls (here of flat Calaveras schist rubble laid in lime mortar) and grooving the stucco to simulate stone construction blocks. An excellent museum and public library occupies the former Krim Hotel building which was built in 1852 of dressed pieces of local gneissic granite and Calaveras schist.

MOKELUMNE HILL

The traveler arriving in Mokelumne Hill is immediately struck by the observation that most of the buildings are made of well finished stone blocks. These are of light brown rhyolite tuff. The I. O. O. F. Hall (Fig. 90) was originally a two story building erected in 1854 by the Adams Express Company. The third story was raised in 1861 by the I. O. O. F. thus making it the first three story building in the Mother Lode. This splendid building, the Mayer building erected 1854 (Fig. 91), the burned-out printing shop (Fig. 92) and the adjoining garage (Fig. 93) all show the beautifully tooled rhyolite tuff block construction. The famed Leger Hotel, reminiscent of the style of the 'fifties (compare with Figs. 4, 58, 110), built of brick and rhyolitic tuff with wooden balconies adjoins the old courthouse which is now part of the hotel (Fig. 94). The exquisite Congregational Church built in 1856 of wood is supported by pillars of fitted rhyolite tuff blocks. The hill which rises west of town was the source of the rhyolite tuff which has here a long surface outcrop in which can be seen the quarry pits opened in the 1850's (Fig. 95).

Two locally famous structures, the Hemmighofen and Suesdorff brewery made of rhyolite tuff, and the Pellaton Store made of adobe bricks are no longer in existence.

JACKSON

Like Sonora, Jamestown, San Andreas, and Placerville, Jackson is a 'forty-nine camp which has successfully made the transition from a boom town to a modern progressive community. Like the others in this class, its main street has assumed a surface veneer of parking meters, new metal trim and glass fronts, but to the person who gives the business houses a second look, many of the buildings show the characteristic features of the 1850's when they were erected.

Jackson is primarily a brick town. After the disastrous early fires, which destroyed the frame structures, brick rather than stone was employed to rebuild a permanent and fireproof town. Among brick structures which are approaching the age of centenarians are the National Hotel (Fig. 96), the Wells Fargo Building (Fig. 97), the Amador County Courthouse (built 1854), the Native Daughters of the Golden West Hall, and a large number of the single story main street stores. Among the better early stone buildings built of meta-andesitic agglomerate which was secured from the basement excavations or hillside quarries is the old Marre Store.

JACKSON GATE

Not far beyond Jackson lies Jackson Gate. Here the main old building is Chichizola's store (Fig. 98) whose thick stone walls have withstood nearly a century's ravages of weather. Just before entering Jackson Gate there are to be seen four tremendous upright wooden wheels whose purpose was to lift mill tailings up the hill for disposal. Their diameters are 68 feet and they are now nearly half a century old.

SUTTER CREEK

Across the highway from the Central Eureka mine on the crest of Sutter Hill is the Botto Granary built in 1869. It is of dressed field stone (andesitic breccia) obtained on the property. With its iron doors and plastered interior, it stands as an excellent example of the enduring architecture of the Mother Lode (Fig. 99). Sutter Creek, like Placerville, has made a valiant effort to modernize its main street, but the quaintness of the 1850 styles as shown by the Sorocco Store, Brignoli Store, American Exchange Hotel, Methodist Church and Masonic Hall cannot be so easily eradicated—these retain the essential simplicity and solidity of the period in which they originated.

Fig. 90. I. O. O. F. Hall, Mokelumne Hill, HABS 1281-2.

Fig. 91. Mayer building, Mokelumne Hill, DMBS Cal-H26.

FIG. 92.   Wall of burned print shop, Mokelumne Hill, DMBS Cal-H27.

FIG. 93.   Print shop and garage, Mokelumne Hill, DMBS Cal-H28.

FIG. 94.   Leger Hotel, Mokelumne Hill, DMBS Cal-H29.

FIG. 95.   Rhyolite tuff quarry, Mokelumne Hill, DMBS Cal-H30.

FIG. 96.   National Hotel and brick store, Jackson HABS 1520.

FIG. 97.   Wells Fargo Office, Jackson, HABS 1156.

FIG. 98.   Chichizola Store, Jackson Gate, HABS 1513.

FIG. 100.   Meta-andesite fieldstone building on hill east of Sutter Creek, DMBS Ama-H3.

FIG. 99.   Left, Botto Granary, Sutter Creek, DMBS Ama-H1; right, detail of dressed meta-andesite blocks, DMBS Ama-H2.

FIG. 101.   Remains of winery east of Sutter Creek on Volcano road, DMBS Ama-H4.

FIG. 102. Stone cellars, same location, DMBS Ama-H5.

FIG. 103. Main Street, Volcano, St. George Hotel on right, HABS 1283-3.

FIG. 104.   Limestone building ruins, Volcano HABS 1504-2.

FIG. 105.   Limestone building, Volcano, DMBS Ama-H5.

FIG. 106.   I. O. O. F. and Masonic buildings, Volcano, HABS 1545.

FIG. 107.   Adams Express Co. building, HABS 1518.

VOLCANO

A side trip east of Sutter Creek via Gopher Gulch will bring the visitor to the most picturesque of all the Mother Lode towns, Volcano (Fig. 103). The town was settled in January 1848 by members of Stevenson's regiment, but not until after the gold discovery at Coloma were the rich "Soldier's Gulch" diggings located.

Three and a quarter miles east of Sutter Creek one sees the remains of an old winery (Figs. 101, 102) built in 1851 of brick and stone (granodiorite, andesite and slate). Beyond, toward Volcano, one sees at every hand crumbling ruins of miner's stone-mud-mortar cabins and the hummocks and pits left by placer miners of the past. The whole country here has literally been turned over in search of gold. Nearing Volcano the limestone cliffs and road cut exposures prepare the visitor for the stone material used in the Volcano buildings. On all sides are massive buildings of quarried and rough-dressed blue limestone (Figs. 104, 105), among the better are the brewery, the Lavezzo Building, the Wells Fargo Building, the Masonic and I. O. O. F. Hall with two stories (Fig. 106), the Adams Express Building (Fig. 107), the old wineshop (Figs. 108, 109). The most imposing building is the charming three-story St. George Hotel of brick with continuous-front balconies (Fig. 110). Here also is the 110 year old cannon "Old Abe" used by the famous Volcano Blues in Civil War times. The Gianinni family of Bank of America fame hails from Volcano, and this town may also boast the first rental library in California (1850).

AMADOR CITY

Through the two blocks of town traversed by Highway 49 one sees on every side the signs of the abandonment of this once thriving city, a contrast to the time when the placers and underground mines produced in abundance. An abandoned brick building stands next to the Fleetheart Store, beautifully constructed of stone whose dressed meta-andesite breccia blocks show the stone masonry techniques of the 'fifties at their best (Fig. 111). At the foot of the main street of Amador City is the old Imperial Hotel, again an example of the beautiful brickwork of California's past.

DRYTOWN

Here is a town, founded in 1848, which has already seen its day of history. In the hills behind Drytown are a score of abandoned mines, their names once household words, now forgotten. As Highway 49 crosses Dry Creek, one may see the brick store built in 1854 (Fig. 112), and across the road the Town Hall (1856) of brick with meta-andesite stone foundations. Down the back road leading east is an equally ancient adobe house, still inhabited, with a dry-laid foundation of meta-andesite which was quarried from the cellar. The Masonic Lodge of brick still remains from the 'fifties.

FIG. 108.   Wineshop, Volcano, DMBS Ama-H6.

FIG. 109.   Detail of doorway of wineshop, Volcano, DMBS Ama-H7.

FIG. 110.   St. George Hotel, Volcano, HABS 1285-2.

FIG. 111.   Stone building, Amador City, DMBS Ama-H8.

PLYMOUTH

Of Plymouth's Gold Rush days when the town was called Pokerville, little meets the visitor's eye: farming has replaced placering as a means of extracting wealth from the earth. About one-half mile out of town on the main road leading west is an old and curiously constructed building with a brick front and rear walls which merge step-like into the side walls constructed of undressed fieldstone of meta-andesite agglomerate (Fig. 113).

FIDDLETOWN

Off the main road a few miles east of Plymouth, is Fiddletown which preserves a considerable measure of its early 1850's flavor. Entering town one sees a dilapidated rammed earth "adobe" (Fig. 114) made by Chinese, a two story brick-covered stone walled store (Fig. 115) and a representative of the common early 1850 style building with a brick front and schist-mud lime mortar walls (Fig. 116). The brick was fired locally, as was the case in nearly every town where the lateritic clays furnished readily available brick earth. Near the east end of town is the Schallhorn Blacksmith and Wagon Shop (Fig. 117), a massive and excellently constructed building erected in 1870 of rectangular hewn blocks (measuring 12 by 18 by 10 inches) of Valley Springs rhyolite tuff which is easily worked when first quarried but hardens after exposure. The source of this tuff, a quarry about 1.5 miles east of Fiddletown, may be seen across a field to the south of the road.

BUTTE CITY

Two and a half miles south of Jackson the old Benoist Store (later owned by Ginnochio), built in 1854, stands beside the road (Fig. 118). It is the only substantial remnant of a once thriving community known as Butte City. The door and window frames are of brick, the walls of Calaveras schist fieldstone and the upper openings still bear the iron-plate doors so familiar to anyone who has any acquaintance with the Gold Rush country.

FIG. 112.   Brick store, Drytown, DMBS Ama-H9.

FIG. 113.   Stone and brick building on west edge of Plymouth, DMBS Ama-H10.

FIG. 114.   Rammed-earth building, Fiddletown DMBS Ama-H11.

FIG. 115.   Brick store, Fiddletown, DMBS Ama-H12.

FIG. 116. Brick building with schist walls, Fiddletown, DMBS Ama-H13.

FIG. 117. Schallhorn smithy, Fiddletown, DMBS Ama-H-14.

FIG. 118. Ginnochio store, Butte City, HABS 1506.

FIG. 120. Four arrastre stones laid in walls of building shown in Fig. 119. Lower left shows drill hole and cross section of stone, DMBS Eld-H2A-D.

FIG. 119. Building foundation walls, near Logtown, DMBS Eld-H1.

FIG. 121. Rhyolite tuff and brick buildings, El Dorado, DMBS Eld-H3.

FIG. 122. Rear of two story stone building shown in Fig. 121, DMBS Eld-H4.

FIG. 123. Tuff-faced meta-andesite building, El Dorado, DMBS Eld-H5.

FIG. 124. Detail of iron-shuttered window and tuff-framed doorway in rear of building shown in Fig. 121, DMBS Eld-H6, H7.

FIG. 125. Rhyolite tuff building, west edge of Diamond Springs, DMBS Eld-H8.

LOGTOWN

Logtown is located in Logtown Ravine about midway between Plymouth and El Dorado. In the little flat near which was once the site of Logtown are two stone house ruins. One, seen through the cottonwoods on the west side of the road (Fig. 119), is of especial interest because laid in the mortared walls of meta-andesite are a number of beautifully polished, mottled granodiorite millstones from an old arrastre (Fig. 120). Fifteen of these arrastre stones average 22 inches long, 15 inches wide, and 10 inches thick. Others even larger occur in the vicinity at random, as though they were too heavy to be of use. On the back surface of the stones are three conjoined drill holes which received iron eye-bolts to which the chains were attached. All show a smooth, undulating, grinding surface marred only by curved scratches formed by contact with the quartz ore. Many have flat or rounded sides which were caused by contact with the sides of the arrastre walls (cf. Fig. 139).

Across the road and up the slope is a second ruin built of granodiorite fieldstone. The door lintel is a heavy, flat slab of schist imported from some other locality.

EL DORADO

Formerly named Mud Springs, El Dorado can boast a larger number of 1850 buildings than many larger Mother Lode towns. The most imposing structure is a group of three buildings of dressed rhyolite tuff built in 1855 (Figs. 121, 122). The westernmost of the three (now a garage) has side walls of fieldstone which is largely meta-andesite agglomerate. The Hill Building now the Wilson garage, erected in 1857 is of the local rhyolite tuff. At the west end of town is a large stone and frame building faced with dressed rhyolite tuff (Fig. 123) and with the walls of meta-andesite fieldstone held in lime mortar. The iron doors and shutters (Fig. 124) are still present, and in the rear is a doorway framed with rhyolite tuff blocks (Fig. 124). Some early brick buildings (Charles Jackson Store, Nathan Rhine's Store and the Gold Nugget building) may also be seen.

DIAMOND SPRINGS

Several buildings erected in the 'fifties still stand in Diamond Springs and are in present day use. The transition from the roaring 'fifties to the prosaic present is exemplified by the old Wells Fargo Express Office now under different management with a sign in front reading "Mom's Kitchen." It is built of attractive gray-brown dressed rhyolite tuff blocks whose source was nearby Pleasant Valley. The site of the famous Golden West Hotel built in 1856 is marked by a vacant lot littered with large dressed facing blocks of rhyolite tuff. Louis Lepetit's Store, erected in 1852, is the modern Red and White Store. Toward the west end of town are two buildings fashioned of dressed rhyolite tuff, one on the south side of the road and now abandoned, the other, used at present as a hay barn (Fig. 125), was originally a general store. The I.O.O.F. Hall, made of wood (1852) rests on a foundation wall of brick with dressed rhyolite tuff corners.

PLACERVILLE

Placerville, a thriving community situated on one of the main trans-Sierran highways (Highway 50) and supported by lumbering, mining, and farming, is, like Auburn and Sonora, a city which has survived and flourished even after the gold placers "played out." Old Dry Diggins or Hangtown, as it has been variously named, contains many of its 1850-1860 period buildings. Many of these are brick such as the famed Ivy House (1861), the Federated Church (1861), and home at 343 Washington Street. The P. G. and E. building (1852) is made of talc schist with brick-trimmed façade. The quarry from which the stone was excavated is the cut directly behind in the hillslope. The Title Building is of similar construction with brick face and talc schist walls. The building at 489 Main Street (built 1861), one door east of the Library, has brick sides, talc schist foundations, and rhyolite tuff facing. The El Dorado County Chamber of Commerce building is made of dressed blocks of rhyolite tuff, probably derived from the Diamond Springs area a few miles to the west. This building was the Pony Express office. Perhaps the nicest of the old buildings is the Wilcox Warehouse (Fig. 126) built of carefully selected blocks of andesite conglomerate and schist.

Hangtowners are conscious of their history, and the visitor will find them and the Chamber of Commerce gracious and helpful hosts. Most of the store windows on the main street contain Gold Rush period antiques.

SHINGLE SPRINGS

Shingle Springs is located about six miles west of El Dorado on Highway 50. The two-story Wells Fargo Building (Fig. 127) made of meta-andesite and semi-dressed granodiorite, both materials common in the immediate vicinity, is the outstanding building of the late 'fifties at Shingle Springs. Just west of town near the railroad crossing, a well preserved house of meta-andesite fieldstone, talc schist, and white quartz float laid with mud-lime mortar can be seen (Fig. 128). South of there a few hundred yards on the French Creek road are two old building ruins made of meta-andesite and serpentine (Fig. 129).

At the beginning of the road from Shingle Springs, which goes north from Highway 50, to Lotus are several old building remnants. A few miles north of Shingle Springs, the first side road to the left leads to Rescue, beyond which, at a distance of two miles on the McDonald (now Reamer) Ranch, are the ruins of an old winery built in the late 'fifties. The construction, of granite fieldstone set in mud-lime mortar, has held up well (Fig. 130). Back on the main road, the next side road to the right takes one east on the Green Valley road, along which are abundant evidences of placer activities for about two miles to the first lane to the right. Two hundred yards down this and to the left are the remains of an earth dam with meta-andesite fieldstone facing, built by miners in the early 'fifties to impound water for placer mining (Fig. 131).

FIG. 126.   Wilcox Warehouse, Placerville, DMBS Eld-H9.

FIG. 127.   Wells Fargo building, Shingle Springs, DMBS Eld-H10.

FIG. 128. Stone house ruin just west of Shingle Springs, DMBS Eld-H11.

FIG. 129. Stone ruin on road to French Creek, DMBS Eld-H12.

FIG. 130. Winery ruins, 2 miles west of Rescue, DMBS Eld-H13.

FIG. 131. Miner's dam of earth and rock, Green Valley road, DMBS Eld-H14.

FIG. 132.   Adam Lohry store, Lotus, DMBS Eld-H15.

FIG. 133.   Granite jail, Coloma, DMBS Eld-H16.

FIG. 134.   Cobblestone building with rhyolite tuff facing, Coloma, DMBS Eld-H17.

FIG. 135.   Robert Bell store, Coloma, DMBS Eld-H18.

LOTUS

Lotus, once called Uniontown, participated in the earliest gold placer activities because of its proximity to Coloma. One quarter of a mile south of Lotus on the west side of the road is the basement remnant of an old building made of rough-quarried granite blocks. Two iron doors still remain as witness of the eighteen-fifties period when it was built. The Uniontown School, built in 1869, is of brick and is still in use. The Adam Lohry Store (Fig. 132) and residence, both built of brick in 1859, are excellent examples of brick structures of the period.

COLOMA

Other Mother Lode towns may claim their own first this or that, but Coloma's historic significance is unequalled as the spot where James Wilson Marshall picked up on January 24, 1848 the first grains of gold in the tailrace of Captain Sutter's sawmill. These bits of gold were the harbingers of the great Gold Rush which is the foundation of our State. Marshall lies buried on the hill where his heroic bronze statute stands. Coloma exists today as a community whose population is less in numbers than its age in years. A number of the old buildings still stand. Among the more interesting is the old jail of the early 'fifties whose three foot thick walls of dressed granite have been partly removed (Fig. 133). Two buildings built about 1860 and now owned by the State Division of Parks, have iron doors, river cobblestone walls and dressed rhyolite tuff facing blocks (Fig. 134). The Robert Bell store of brick constructed about 1856 (Fig. 135) and Bekeart's Store of brick built in 1853 (Fig. 136) are still standing. On the back streets may be seen fences of piled rhyolite tuff blocks which came from an old winery operating in the 'sixties. Several of the old wooden buildings in and around Coloma are built, in part, of lumber cut in the now-vanished Sutter sawmill in 1850-53.

MEYER'S DANCE HALL

Just above Lotus, after crossing the South Fork of the American River, about a mile and a half below the spot where James Marshall discovered gold in 1848, one sees to the left the splendid two story stone ruin of Meyer's Dance Hall and Saloon (Fig. 137). The walls are of granite fieldstone or river boulders split so as to furnish a flat facing. The corners, door and window frames are of dressed rhyolite tuff blocks. Source of this tuff was probably to the south in the vicinity of Diamond Springs. A half mile beyond on the left side of the road is a foundation built into the sidehill next to the road. It is of split granite fieldstone laid with lime mortar. About a half mile on and just past a prosperous farm, is a complex of stone foundations made of granite fieldstone laid with lime mortar. After crossing the next bridge, there may be seen along the stream terrace to the left several ruins of granite fieldstone buildings (Fig. 138).

FIG. 136.   Bekeart's store, Coloma, DMBS Eld-H19.

FIG. 137.   Meyer's Dance Hall and Saloon, just north of Lotus, DMBS Pla-H1.

FIG. 138.   Stone ruins between Lotus and Pilot Hill along creek, DMBS Pla-H2.

FIG. 139.   Arrastre walls, 1 mile north of Baileys, DMBS Pla-H3.

PILOT HILL

Of Pilot Hill little remains except a few scattered remnants of stone cellars. Just beyond on the left is Baileys and the picturesque three story porticoed brick inn, now owned privately. One mile above Baileys on the left side of the road across the creek is one of the few remaining old arrastres of the Mother Lode. The mill basin (Fig. 139) is nine feet in diameter and two feet high and constructed of white quartz. The heavy mill stones or "drags" have been removed, and a few lie scattered on the surface nearby.

COOL

Five miles north of Baileys near the site of Cool are some old lime kilns which operated in the 'sixties. The two kilns on the right side of the road have straight faces and curved sides. They are constructed of dressed limestone blocks and lined with quarried meta-andesite which was more heat resistant (Fig. 140). The ruins of several building foundations made of the same limestone which was burned in the kilns are nearby, and the quarry pit may be clearly seen. Just beyond is the modern Cragco Company quarry.

KELSEY

At the little town of Kelsey, six miles north of Placerville, on Highway 93 to Georgetown, a frame cabin has been reconstructed on the site once occupied by the blacksmithy of James Marshall, famed as the original discoverer of gold at Coloma. This cabin once housed a museum, the only remaining exhibit of which is a granodiorite muller stone from an old arrastre, the primitive manual mill employed by Mexicans in the very first efforts in California to reduce gold from hard rock ores (Fig. 141).

LOUISVILLE

A mile and a half north of Kelsey, at the abandoned settlement of Louisville, is the ruins of a house, made of slabs of laminated schist set in mud mortar (Fig. 142).

GEORGETOWN

Georgetown, on Highway 93 ten miles north of Kelsey and once known as "Growlersburg," is one of the towns located in areas having abundant lateritic brick clays, and this natural feature is reflected in the choice of building materials. No stone buildings are to be seen nor are there foundations or fences of stone.

The present I. O. O. F. Hall, formerly an hotel managed by Madame Balsar, is a two story brick building erected in 1859. It has been remodeled twice. The row of brick buildings along the north side of the main street includes one which functioned as a Union Armory during the Civil War.

GREENWOOD

The little community of Greenwood 5.5 miles west of Georgetown on Highway 93, contains a few vestiges of its halcyon days. A ruined wine cellar, dug into the hillside and with its doorway framed with blocks of meta-andesitic agglomerate can be seen on the west side of the main street. Directly across the street there are two building foundations made of slabs of schist set in mud mortar (Fig. 143). In front of the house numbered 308 there are two fragments of a granodiorite stone "drag" from an arrastre. In recent times they have served as hitching posts. On the east side of the highway at the north end of town there is the foundation of a long narrow building made of blocks of fieldstone of meta-andesite agglomerate and Mariposa slate.

AUBURN RAVINE

On the old Sacramento highway, a mile west of Auburn, a few building ruins mark the former settlement of Auburn Ravine. The outstanding remains to be seen are those of a composite brick and stone building which was once a saloon. One section of the structure is made of blocks of schist set in mud mortar (Fig. 144), the second section is of bricks set in lime mortar (Fig. 145). Adjacent to this building, the walls of a semi-subterranean "cold house" can still be seen. It is made of dry-laid blocks of schist.

AUBURN

Auburn is one of the most vigorous of the surviving Gold Rush towns. Located at the intersection of highways 49 and 40, its expansion eastward up the hill has left a number of early buildings undisturbed in the old town at the foot of the hill. The building of the J. E. Cory & Son Feed Company in the 100 block of Lincoln Way is constructed of schist blocks (Figs. 148, 149). It has ornamental arches over the second story windows made of sawed soapstone blocks (Fig. 150). The adjacent brick building rests on a schist foundation. The opposite corner building of the Auburn Electric Company is built of thick slabs of schist (Fig. 146). Extending up Court Street from this building is a row of three old brick structures, and directly across the street is a small abandoned building made of schist slabs (Fig. 151). Lincoln Way, from Court Street south, contains a number of old brick buildings notable among which is the round front of the Union Bar (Fig. 147).

West of Auburn on the foothill fringes of the Sacramento Valley are several mining towns dating from the 'fifties. Among these are Ophir, Penryn, Gold Hill and Virginiatown. At this last place are two splended rammed-earth adobes (Fig. 152) built by Armour in 1852, and the original home of the present meat packing concern.

Fig. 140.   Lime kilns near Cool, DMBS Pla-H4.

Fig. 141.   Arrastre stone of granodiorite, Kelsey, DMBS Pla-H5.

FIG. 142.   Schist slab house ruin, Louisville, DMBS Pla-H6.

FIG. 143.   Schist building foundations, Greenwood, DMBS Pla-H7.

FIG. 144.   Brick and schist building ruin, Auburn Ravine, DMBS Pla-H8.

FIG. 145.   Placer Herald and other brick buildings, Auburn, DMBS Pla-H9.

Fig. 146.   Auburn Electric Co. Building, Auburn, DMBS Pla-H10.

Fig. 147.   Union Bar, Oldtown in Auburn, DMBS Pla-H11.

FIG. 149. Detail of arched doorway of Cory Feedstore, Auburn, DMBS Pla-H13.

FIG. 151. Schist building on Court Street, Auburn, DMBS Pla-H15.

FIG. 148. Rear wall of Cory Feedstore, Auburn, DMBS Pla-H12.

FIG. 150. Sawed soapstone window arch Cory Feedstore, Auburn, DMBS Pla-H14.

FIG. 152.   Rammed-earth adobe, Virginiatown,
DMBS Pla-H16.

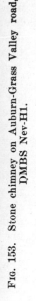

FIG. 153.   Stone chimney on Auburn-Grass Valley road,
DMBS Nev-H1.

FIG. 154.   Arched winery cellar door, 2 miles south of Grass Valley, DMBS Nev-H2.

WOLF ROAD JUNCTION

Ten miles north of Auburn at the road junction leading to Wolf stands a well constructed chimney (Fig. 153), the remnant of a large house. It is made of laminated chert set in mud-lime mortar and the fireplace is lined with fired brick.

One and a half miles farther on and to the left in the edge of the flat, stands another chimney constructed of rough serpentine chunks.

Elsewhere to the south the buildings originally erected with these chimneys would have been of stone, but Nevada County, with its timber and early sawmills, turned to frame construction, a cultural feature which is responsible for the scarcity of stone buildings in the Northern Diggings.

GRASS VALLEY

Grass Valley lies in a pine-forested region, and not long after the discovery of rich placer and quartz mines there were several sawmills operating here. Frame houses characterized the early architecture, but a disastrous fire in 1855 led, as all through the Mother Lode country, to the building of fireproof structures. The unavailability of the excellent meta-andesite used so extensively farther south for stone buildings and the abundance of lateritic clays which served as brick earth are in part responsible for the choice of brick as the material for durable buildings in Grass Valley. To the Mother Lode traveler who by now has seen a number of brick buildings, the familiar style will be immediately apparent on the main business street of Grass Valley in the many store fronts. The Club Cafe building is an outstanding large stone structure made of serpentine and talc schist held in lime mortar (Fig. 155). A few blocks south of the main street on Mill Street is a beautifully built mill building (Fig. 156) of rough serpentine, talc schist, and granite blocks laid in lime mortar. The window and doorframes are of brick. Nearby, across the street from the Lola Montez house is a dwelling (Fig. 157) constructed in a style similar to that of the mill building. One distinctive stylistic trait of the local architecture is leaving the outer wall of the brick fireplace chimneys flush with the outer wall of stone buildings (cf. Fig. 157).

About two miles south of Grass Valley on the west side of the road are the remains of a winery built of rough-quarried granite blocks set in mud mortar. Several complete buildings still stand. Figure 154 shows the brick-arched entrance to one of the cellars.

NEVADA CITY

Like many other settlements of the Mother Lode, Nevada City has acquired a surface veneer of modern life, but has still not lost the peculiar charm which pervades these century-old towns. This charm derives from and persists by reason of the old buildings which still form the physical core of present business activities. Nevada City, like its age-mates farther south and north, is a holdover, a tarriant, from the booming 'fifties. And not until the old brick and stone buildings are torn down and the towns laid out with a view to convenience will they lose their particular flavor—the Mother Lode town is something unique, and something with universal appeal. This observation we submit as important, since too many visitors (and guidebooks) are overimpressed with the romantic history which takes the form of a recital of lynchings, the size of gold nuggets found, or how many million dollars in gold dust passed through the doors of this or that building, and thereby fail to appreciate the country and the old cities for what they are.

The largest stone building here is the old brewery (Fig. 158), now a cafe, built of quarried undressed granite. In the wall facing the alley may be seen the distinctive trait of leaving the brick chimney flush with the outer face of the main wall. The two-story brick firehouse (Fig. 159) and the Ott Assay Office built in 1851 (now covered with a stucco front) are typical of the early brick architecture of Nevada City. The common stone in this area is granite, and one will see numerous retaining walls along the sloping streets of this material.

TOWNS IN VICINITY OF FRENCH CORRAL

West of Grass Valley on Highway 15 lies Rough and Ready, first occupied in 1848, and during the Civil War the scene of a local secessionist flurry. There are no outstanding stone buildings in Rough and Ready. Beyond is Timbuctoo, named, it is said, for the birthplace of a negro slave settler, which still exhibits one excellent brick-fronted, fieldstone-walled store built in the early 'fifties. Turning east on the way to French Corral one passes over the Middle Fork of the Yuba in the famous covered bridge. Bridgeport can boast many excellent dry-laid granite walls and fences.

Two lone brick buildings mark the permanent remains of French Corral. The Milton Mining and Water Company Building, which also served as the Wells Fargo Express Office (Fig. 160) is remarkably well preserved. Here in 1877, according to a brass plate affixed to its front, the Ridge Telephone Company operated the first long distance telephone line in the world. The line connected French Corral via Sweetland, North San Juan, North Columbia Hill, North Bloomfield and Graniteville with Milton and Bowman Lake, 58 miles away. The second brick building, which now serves as a barn, was a store (Fig. 161). Four miles beyond the traveler comes again to Highway 49 and not far north is North San Juan.

FIG. 155.   Club Cafe building (side wall), Grass Valley, DMBS Nev-H3.

FIG. 156.   Mill building, Grass Valley, DMBS Nev-H4.

FIG. 157.   Stone house on Mill St., Grass Valley, DMBS Nev-H5.

FIG. 158.   Stone brewery, Sacramento St., Nevada City, DMBS Nev-H6.

FIG. 159.   Brick firehouse, Nevada City, DMBS Nev-H7.

FIG. 160.   Milton Mining and Water Co. building, French Corral, DMBS Nev-H8.

FIG. 161.   Brick store, French Corral, DMBS Nev-H9.

FIG. 162.   Wells Fargo Station (now Forty-Niner Cafe) and Masonic Hall,
North San Juan, HABS, 1697.

FIG. 163.   Detail of stone addition to brick building, North San Juan, DMBS Nev-H10.

FIG. 164.   Sidewall of office building, North San Juan, DMBS Nev-H11

1

FIG. 165.   Detail of arched doorways and grillwork, North San Juan, DMBS Nev-H12.

FIG. 166.   Pioneer Museum building, Downieville, HABS, 1687.

FIG. 167.   Building behind Ponta Hotel, Downieville, DMBS Sie-H1.

FIG. 168.   Dry-laid schist wall, Downieville, DMBS Sie-H2.

NORTH SAN JUAN

North San Juan is composed almost entirely of brick structures. All of them date from the 1850's. The 49'er Cafe on the corner is the old Wells Fargo Company Office. The adjoining two story building, now a store and bar, is the Masonic Hall (Fig. 162). What is now Bryan's Garage was the San Juan Times Building. The main structure is brick, but attached to the rear is an addition built of rough granite rubble set in lime mortar (Fig. 163), one of the very rare examples of stone construction in this brick town. Nowhere is the brick architecture better displayed than in the two story building just east of the 49'er Cafe, with cast iron grillwork running around the face about halfway up the side (Figs. 164, 165). Two of the arched brick doorways have been joined with a wooden arch to admit automobiles when the building was converted to a garage. The lower floor originally housed a store and the upper floor was occupied by offices of the various local hydraulic mining companies. Across the street is a row of single story commercial buildings such as may be seen in nearly every other Sierran Gold Belt town.

The bricks were made locally and appear to be unusually firm. Their excellence is in part due to the good clay and the tempering material which is decomposed granite.

Just above North San Juan near where Highway 49 crosses the Middle Fork of the Yuba River can be seen the remains of the Freeman Toll Bridge. On each side of the river still stand the huge quarried granite abutments. On the north bank is a fine old building built of well dressed granite blocks, and in the general vicinity a number of well made dry rock granite boulder fences made by Chinese in the 'sixties.

DOWNIEVILLE

This Gold Rush town marks the northern limit of our survey. The Courthouse which burned recently still exhibits remnants of its stone basement and separate outbuilding of boulders and brick. The iron cell-blocks, reminiscent of the Knights Ferry jail, stands amid the courthouse ruins. The Pioneer Museum building made of carefully selected schist slabs and with brick doorframes (Fig. 166) dates from the early 'fifties. In the rear of the frame Ponta Hotel is a stone cellar (Fig. 167) built of schist slabs and river boulders held in mud mortar. This structure dates from the 'sixties. Downieville is built in a steep walled canyon with a narrow bottom, and the standard method of securing building space has been to erect retaining walls to form flat terraces. Excellent dry-laid terrace walls may be seen on both sides of the river; a typical example is shown in Fig. 168.

BIBLIOGRAPHY

AVERILL, CHARLES V., and others, Placer mining for gold in California: California Div. Mines Bull. 135, 377 pp., 1946.

BORTHWICK, J. D., Three years in California: W. Blackwood and Sons, 384 pp., Edinburgh and London, 1857. Reprinted 1917 as *The Gold Hunters* edited by Horace Kephart: Outing Pub. Co., Cleveland and New York.

BUCKBEE, EDNA B., The saga of old Tuolumne: R. R. Wilson, 526 pp., New York, 1935.

CALIFORNIA HISTORICAL SOCIETY, Centennial papers: Spec. Pub. 21, 56 pp., San Francisco, 1947.

DRURY, AUBREY, California, an intimate guide: Harper and Bros.: 592 pp., New York, 1947.

GLASSCOCK, C. B., A golden highway: The Bobbs-Merrill Co., 313 pp., Indianapolis, 1934.

JOHNSTON, PHILIP, Lost and living cities of the California gold rush, California centennials guide: Touring Bureau, Automobile Club of Southern California, 61 pp., Los Angeles, 1948.

RENSCH, H. E., HOOVER, MILDRED B., and others, Historic spots in California, valley and Sierra counties: Stanford Univ. Press and Cambridge Univ. Press, 568 pp., Palo Alto and Cambridge, 1933.

STELLMAN, LOUIS J., Mother lode, the story of California's gold rush days: Harr-Wagner Pub. Co., 304 pp., San Francisco, 1934.

WESTON, OTHETO, Mother Lode album: Stanford Univ. Press., 177 pp., 2 plates, 204 photos, Palo Alto, 1948.